DEDICATION

This book is dedicated to all the citizens of the United States of America who have made this program of interplanetary exploration possible and who, along with all mankind, will benefit from the increased awareness of the universe and how the Earth and its peoples relate to it.

NASA SP-396

PIONEER ODYSSEY

RICHARD O. FIMMEL
Pioneer Project
Ames Research Center

WILLIAM SWINDELL
Optical Sciences Laboratory
University of Arizona

ERIC BURGESS
Science Writer

Prepared at Ames Research Center

Scientific and Technical Information Office   1977
NATIONAL AERONAUTICS AND SPACE ADMINISTRATION
Washington, D.C.

☆ U.S. GOVERNMENT PRINTING OFFICE : 1976 O — 221–621

For sale by the Superintendent of Documents,
U.S. Government Printing Office, Washington, D.C. 20402
Price $9.85 Stock Number 033–000–00662–4

Contents

Foreword

THERE ARE CERTAIN human enterprises that seem, from the very beginning, to be touched with a certain elan that distinguishes them from others. Those of us who have had the pleasure to be associated with the Pioneer project have long felt that it belongs in this group. There is about Pioneer 10 and 11 a simplicity in concept and an elegance in design and execution that clearly transcends the ordinary.

These Pioneer spacecraft are unique: Pioneer 10 is the first spacecraft to fly beyond the orbit of Mars and through the Asteroid belt, it made the first series of "in situ" measurements of Jupiter's environment, it provided the first close-up pictures of the giant planet and finally, Pioneer 10 is the first man-made object to leave the solar system. Pioneer 11 is the first spacecraft to fly to the ringed planet Saturn.

In spite of the essential simplicity of the Pioneer spacecraft, highly sophisticated scientific experiments were performed. The first direct measurements of Jupiter's magnetic field and of the charged particles trapped in the field were performed. A thermal map of Jupiter was obtained and information about the composition of the planet's upper atmosphere was secured. The trajectory of Pioneer 10 was such that the spacecraft was occulted by the satellite Io which provided the first direct evidence of the very tenuous atmosphere that surrounds Io by observing the direct alteration of the telemetry signal carrier wave. The trajectory of Pioneer 11 provided the first pictures of the polar regions of the giant planet. These results, as well as many others, are explained in more detail in this volume.

It would be a mistake to dwell only on the scientific results of these Pioneers without mentioning the engineering achievements. Both spacecraft have transmitted information over telemetry links for distances that are by now almost an order of magnitude larger than those transmitted by any previous spacecraft. The radioisotope thermoelectric power supplies aboard Pioneer are more efficient and longer lasting than previous designs. Finally, the integration and the management of the large number of diverse experiments was an important engineering achievement.

This Pioneer project proved that a complex and sophisticated planetary exploration mission can be carried out at a relatively moderate cost. It is likely that the management of future planetary missions will follow some of the methods that were developed by the Pioneer project. This is especially important in view of the fact that funds for exploration projects of this kind are likely to become much harder to obtain in the coming years.

In spite of the obvious importance of the scientific results, the engineering achievements and the management techniques, the meaning of Pioneer transcends them in importance. The Pioneer mission to the outer planets is a symbol of human aspirations. To reach out, to explore, to satisfy the curiosity, that is what is really important. Pioneer proves once again that we can move in the right direction and that real achievements are possible. This volume is a tribute to those who worked so hard to demonstrate this point.

Hans Mark, Director
NASA-Ames Research Center
Moffett Field, California
August 1974

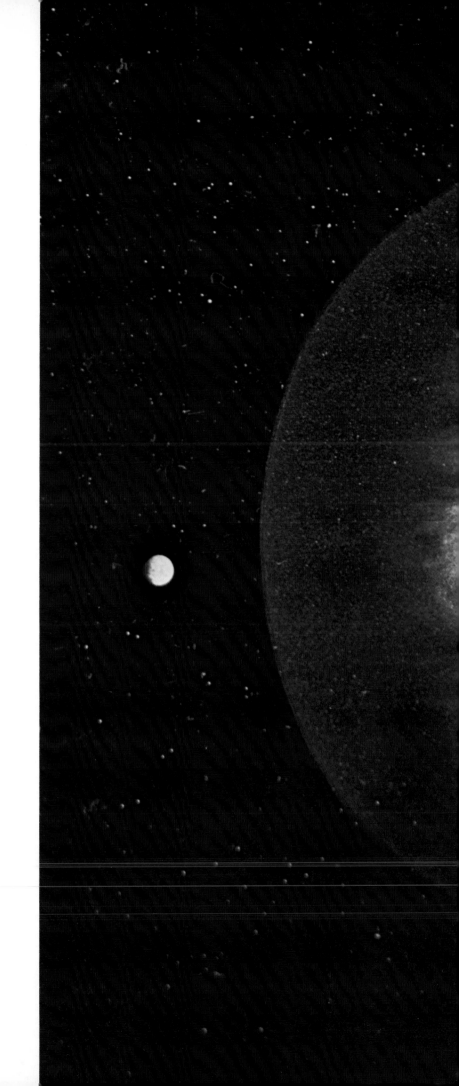

Introduction

ANCIENT PEOPLES, perhaps thousands of years ago, undoubtedly conceived the idea of "reaching out" to Jupiter, the largest and most brilliant of the "wandering stars." But for mankind to stretch across the half billion miles to the giant planet of the Solar System many advances in technical and organizational fields of human endeavor had to be made. Outreach to Jupiter did not become a serious possibility until the Pioneer F and G Project was formed by NASA early in 1968. And then man began to design an extension of his senses that would probe the environs of the giant of the Solar System, a truly pioneer odyssey into the virtually unknown regions beyond the orbit of Mars.

In the ensuing years, a dedicated and cooperative effort of several thousand people in Government, university, and private industrial organizations converted the idea into a reality. Less than twelve generations after Galileo first saw the banded disc of Jupiter and the flickering dots of its large satellites in the newly invented telescope, mankind sent a machine to make observations within that Jovian system.

The two Pioneer spacecraft for the mission to Jupiter each weighed only about 570 pounds, yet carried eleven highly sophisticated instruments capable of operating unattended for many years in space. The spacecraft consumes less electrical power than a standard 100 watt lamp yet is able to accept instructions from Earth to control numerous operating modes of its scientific payload, process observations from these scientific instruments and format the observations into information usable on Earth. Even more remarkable, the spacecraft transmits a radio signal of only 8 watts power — equal to a nightlight — yet the information carried by the radio signal is received back on Earth from a distance of several billion miles.

The Pioneer mission could not have been a success without the special engineering, scientific and management organization created for its accomplishment. This organization was rather unique in that it first had to meet a launch date target relatively quickly and then had to function for an extremely long mission operational time, far longer than any previous missions to planets. The first task was thus to organize so that the mission could be planned and the spacecraft designed and fabricated to be ready for launch within a few weeks of a 30-month target for completion.

The program also produced an organization that planned mission operations to such detail that more than 16,000 commands were transmitted flawlessly to the distant spacecraft during Jupiter encounter. And each command reached the spacecraft within one second of the planned time despite the more than 90 minutes required for the radio message to travel from Earth to the spacecraft and for the spacecraft to return a confirmation to controllers back on Earth.

The organization for Pioneer also determined the required flight path from Earth to Jupiter with such precision, and controlled the launch vehicle with such accuracy, that 21 months after launch the spacecraft was able to fly behind Jupiter's satellite Io, thereby providing the first measurement that indicated the possibility of a tenuous atmosphere about this large satellite.

Finally, the Pioneer organization processed and analyzed each year sufficient information from the spacecraft to fill a book having about 3 million pages and reduced this avalanche of data from space into summaries of manageable size.

And all this organization depended on people, consisted of people: the people who really made this whole mission possible.

Pioneer has always depended on the dedication of many individuals from many organizations throughout the world to achieve its scientific objectives, and, as evidenced by the success of the Pioneer series, this dependence is completely justified.

Relatively few individuals have an opportunity during their lives to participate in such a challenging, historic, pioneering effort; and still fewer are able to enjoy the rewards of such an activity. We who have worked on Pioneer 10 and its sister spacecraft, Pioneer 11, consider ourselves fortunate to be in both classes. For the opportunity we thank the people of the United States of America, who have supported our country's space effort and its spreading of human awareness of a vast and intriguing universe in which our own unique planet Earth is only one of myriads of worlds. This volume describing the mission to Jupiter and its results is one of the many rewards for our effort which we share with you, the reader.

Charles F. Hall
Pioneer Project Manager
NASA-Ames Research Center

Acknowledgements

IN THE PREPARATION of this book, the authors gratefully acknowledge having drawn upon the work of many others too numerous to mention individually. Many scientists and project staff personnel provided interviews for researching material for the book. Of particular importance was valuable assistance in the form of initial suggestions and later comments on all or parts of drafts of the book by John V. Foster, Tom Gehrels, Robert U. Hofstetter, Joseph E. Lepetich, Norman J. Martin, Robert R. Nunamaker, Gilbert A. Schroeder, Peter Waller, and John H. Wolfe.

Personnel from NASA Ames Research Center Pioneer Project staff, Technical Information Division and Photo Technology Branch were particularly helpful in providing information and research material and producing the book. NASA Headquarters Scientific and Technical Information Office made publication possible within so short a time after analysis of the Pioneer 10 results.

The authors are also indebted to personnel of the Lunar and Planetary Laboratory and the Optical Sciences Center of the University of Arizona for astronomical information and photographs and the production of the images of Jupiter and its satellites reproduced in this book. Special thanks must go to Yin-pao Chen, Peter H. Smith, and John Kendall (computer processing), Rodney A. Norden (image display), and John W. Fountain (photographic processing). Additionally, Lyn Doose of the University of Arizona provided material on the Great Red Spot from his doctoral thesis, and Mary Ann Breen of Keith Cole Photography provided valuable processing assistance in sizing and color correcting Pioneer 10 Jupiter images for publication.

AUTHORS' PREFACE TO NEW EDITION

THE SUCCESS OF PIONEER 11 in repeating an encounter with the giant planet Jupiter and producing unique images of the north polar regions of the planet necessitated an updating of SP-349. Additional material has been added to the descriptive material about the flight of the spacecraft in Chapter 5. The following chapter, describing the results of the two missions, has been completely updated in the light of further interpretations of the Pioneer 10 data coupled with the new data from Pioneer 11. An additional Chapter 9 has been added to provide a selection of the better images obtained by Pioneer 11. This chapter also includes images of the four Galilean satellites. The bibliography has been updated to include scientific papers published since the original edition.

Figure 1-1. Important to the ancient Babylonians, the brilliant planet Jupiter ruled the night sky and mapped out the Zodiacal constellations.

1
Jupiter, Giant of the Solar System

IN ROMAN AND GREEK MYTHOLOGY the god Jupiter was accepted as the most powerful and capricious ruler of the heavens; no wonder ancient astronomers gave the same name to the planet that year after year so brilliantly rules the night sky. After the Sun and the Moon, Jupiter is, indeed, the most spectacular object in the sky. Although Venus is at times brighter it cannot ride the midnight sky as does Jupiter.

Today's astronomers acknowledge Jupiter as being perhaps the most important planet of the Solar System. It is the largest and most massive. After the Sun — the star about which all bodies of the Solar System revolve — Jupiter contains two-thirds of the matter in the Solar System. Orbiting the Sun at an average distance of 779 million km (484 million mi.), Jupiter is some 5.2 times as far away as Earth.

Cuneiforms of the Babylonian epic *Enuma Elish* or Tablets of Creation refer to Jupiter in the Fifth Tablet as the marker of the signs of the Zodiac . . . "He (Marduk — the Creator) founded the station of Nibir (Jupiter) to determine their bounds . . ." To the Babylonians, Nibir was the special name for Jupiter when the planet appeared directly opposite to the Sun and thus shone high and brightly in the midnight sky over the fertile valley of the Euphrates. Since Jupiter travels around its orbit once in almost 12 years, the planet each year moves eastward to occupy the next constellation of the Zodiac. Also, as a result of the relative motions of Earth and Jupiter around the Sun, the faster moving Earth overtakes Jupiter and thereby causes the planet each year to trace out a third of the Zodiacal constellation, i.e., 10 degrees of arc, in a westward, or retrograde, direction relative to the stars (Figure 1-1).

(a)

(b)

(c)

(d)

(e)

(f)

(g)

Planets of the Solar System consist of two types: small, dense, inner planets with solid surfaces — Mercury, Venus, Earth with its Moon, and Mars — and large, mainly gaseous, outer planets — Jupiter, Saturn, Uranus, and Neptune, with some satellites as big as the smaller inner planets. Pluto, the outermost known planet, cannot be observed well enough from Earth to be accurately classified, though it is believed to be more like the inner than the outer planets in size.

Between the orbits of Mars and Jupiter, like a transition zone dividing the inner from the outer Solar System, is a wide belt of asteroids, or minor planets, the largest of which, Ceres, is only 1022 km (635 mi.) in diameter. Most asteroids are smaller and many seem to be irregularly shaped.

The first decade of space exploration concentrated on the inner Solar System (Figure 1-2), but at the beginning of the second decade scientists and space technologists started to look at missions to the outer planets. The old fascination of mankind, brilliant Jupiter, became the target for the first mission beyond Mars.

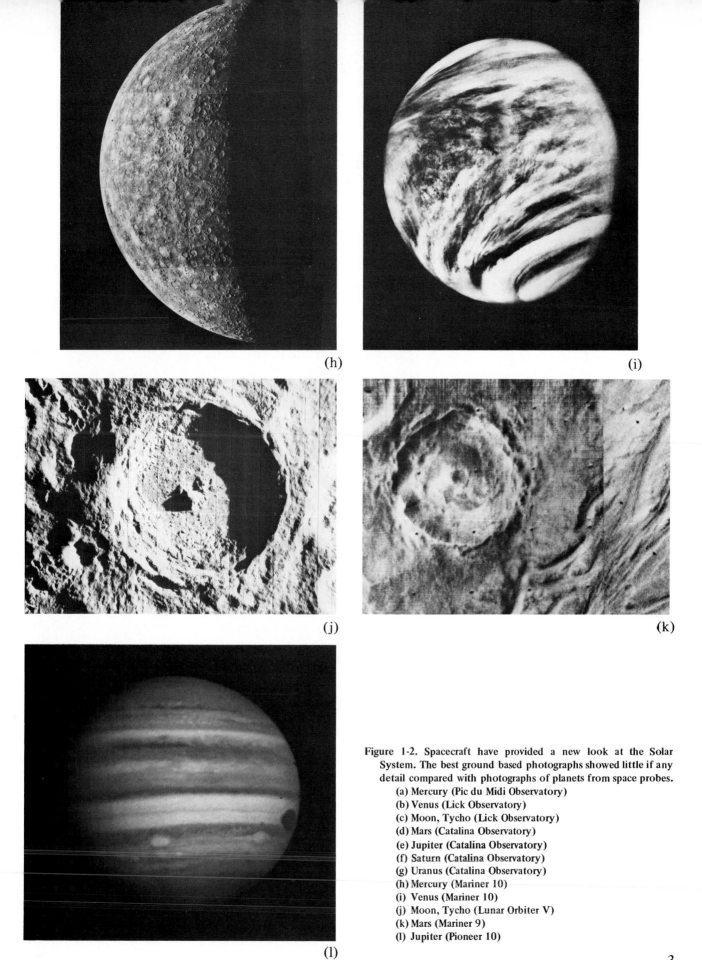

(h)

(i)

(j)

(k)

(l)

Figure 1-2. Spacecraft have provided a new look at the Solar System. The best ground based photographs showed little if any detail compared with photographs of planets from space probes.

(a) Mercury (Pic du Midi Observatory)
(b) Venus (Lick Observatory)
(c) Moon, Tycho (Lick Observatory)
(d) Mars (Catalina Observatory)
(e) Jupiter (Catalina Observatory)
(f) Saturn (Catalina Observatory)
(g) Uranus (Catalina Observatory)
(h) Mercury (Mariner 10)
(i) Venus (Mariner 10)
(j) Moon, Tycho (Lunar Orbiter V)
(k) Mars (Mariner 9)
(l) Jupiter (Pioneer 10)

3

Figure 1-3. Jupiter is the dominant planet of the Solar System. The terrestrial planets, Mercury, Venus, Earth, and Mars are relatively small compared with the outer giants, Jupiter, Saturn, Uranus and Neptune.

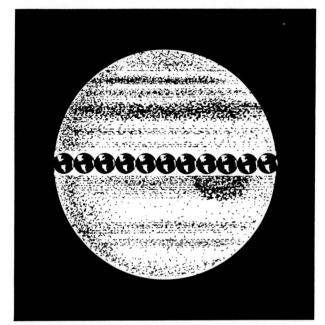

Figure 1-4. A whole series of Earths could be strung along the equator of Jupiter like beads.

Dominant Position of Jupiter

Jupiter is an unusual planet by terrestrial standards, both in size and composition. Only slightly denser than water, Jupiter is 317.8 times more massive than Earth. Secondary only to the Sun itself, the giant planet dominates the Solar System (Figure 1-3). Its gravity affects the orbits of other planets and may have prevented the asteroids from coalescing into a planet. Many comets are pulled by Jupiter into distorted orbits, and some of the short period comets appear to have become controlled by Jupiter so that their orbits have their most distant points from the Sun about the distance of the orbit of the giant planet.

Although Jupiter is big (Figure 1-4), it is not big enough to have become a second sun, being too small for its own weight to raise its central temperature high enough for a nuclear reaction to be triggered in its core. However, had Jupiter been 60 to 100 times its present size, our Solar System might have become a binary star system, like so many other stellar systems; and nighttime would have been infrequent on Earth. As it is, Jupiter emits several times more energy than it receives from the Sun, energy probably derived from continued cooling of the planet following its primordial gravitational collapse eons ago when the Solar System formed. A continuing gravitational collapse at a present rate of 1 millimeter per year could alternatively provide the observed heat output from Jupiter.

Family of Satellites

Early in the seventeenth century news spread across Europe of an astounding invention by a spectacle-maker, Hans Lippershey of Middelburgh, Holland. Using a convex and a concave lens at opposite ends of a tube, he made remote objects appear nearer. Two men acted on this news and separately constructed telescopes as the new invention was called. Looking at Jupiter they were astounded to discover that the bright planet possessed a system of satellites — an undreamed of condition in the Aristotelean world of Earth-centered philosophy holding sway at that time. In fact, some scientists of that day claimed the luminous objects were defects of the new instrument, not real objects.

5

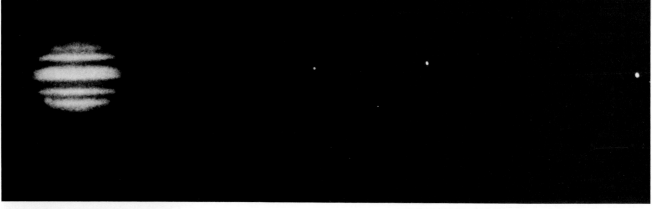

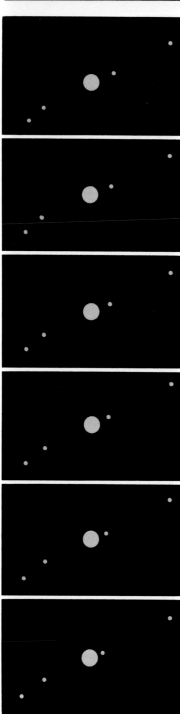

Figure 1-5. Jupiter and its four Galilean satellites present a fine sight, even in good field glasses. Some sharp-eyed people claim they can see these satellites with their unaided eyes. The photograph at top of page shows a typical configuration; right to left the satellites are: Europa, Ganymede, and Callisto. Io is obscured by the planet. (Catalina Observatory)

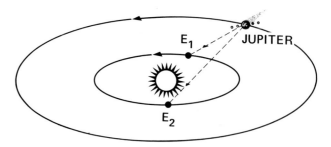

Figure 1-6. Each year as the Earth moves around its orbit, the times of eclipse of Jupiter's satellites become late. This is because light takes nearly 16 minutes longer to cross the orbit of the Earth. In 1675 the Danish astronomer Roemer determined the velocity of light from this effect.

The discovery of these satellites of Jupiter (Figure 1-5) is usually accredited to Galilei Galileo, who published the results of an observation made at Padua on January 7, 1610. Some historians claim, however, that it was Simon Marius of Ausbach, Germany, who first observed the Jovian satellites on December 29, 1609; but he did not publish his observation. These satellites were later given the names Io, Europa, Ganymede, and Callisto by Marius, but are often referred to as the Galilean satellites. Today the satellites are frequently identified by the Roman numerals I, II, III, and IV, respectively.

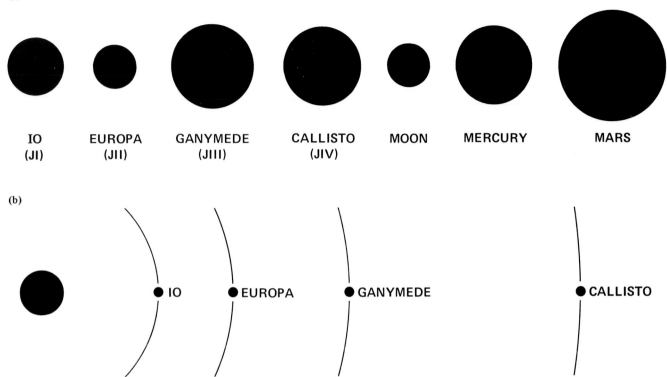

Figure 1-7. The large satellites of Jupiter rival the smaller planets in size. (a) The relative sizes of the satellites. (b) The relative distances from Jupiter.

One of the most important discoveries in physics was made by the Danish astronomer, Ole Roemer, by means of Jupiter's satellites. Astronomers had observed that the eclipses of Jovian satellites occur 16 minutes and 40 seconds late when Jupiter is on the far side of the Sun from the Earth. In 1675, while in Paris, Roemer explained that this delay results from the finite velocity of light. Light traveling across Earth's orbit, when Earth is farthest from Jupiter, takes 16 minutes and 40 seconds to cover the additional distance. He thereby measured the velocity of light as being about 300,000 km (186,000 mi.) per second (Figure 1-6).

The Galilean satellites of Jupiter are quite large bodies (Figure 1-7). Two of the satellites, Callisto and Ganymede, are about the size of the planet Mercury, while Io and Europa rival Earth's Moon. All four satellites are easily seen through a pair of field glasses, appearing as star-like objects nearly in a straight line on either side of the disc of the planet because their orbits are viewed almost edgewise from Earth. Some people with acute vision have been able to see the satellites with their unaided eyes — a good test for sharp vision. The best time to do this is when the sky is still faintly light following sunset, before the planet becomes too brilliant in a black sky.

A fifth satellite of Jupiter was not discovered until almost three centuries later — by E. E. Barnard in 1892. Today, Jupiter is known to have at least fourteen satellites — the other ten are much smaller bodies than the four Galilean satellites. The Jovian system thus resembles a miniature solar system, except that the outermost four satellites of Jupiter orbit oppositely to the others, whereas all the planets go around the Sun in the same direction.

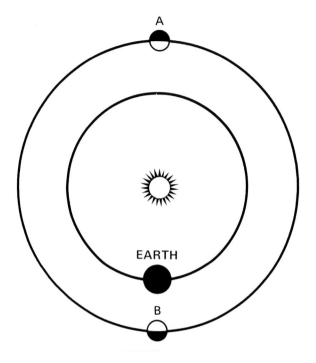

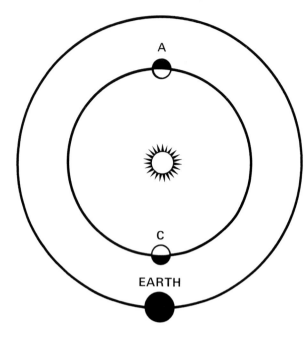

SUPERIOR PLANETS   INFERIOR PLANETS

Figure 1-8. When superior planets as seen from Earth are on the far side of the Sun they are said to be in superior conjunction (A). When opposite to the Sun in Earth's skies, they are then closest to Earth and said to be in opposition (B). Inferior planets can never be in opposition but instead attain inferior conjunction (C), i.e., are between Earth and Sun.

Solar Orbit of Jupiter and Appearance in Earth's Skies

Ancient astronomers, observing the motions of planets against the background of stars, called them wandering stars. The word "planet" is derived from the Greek word "wanderer." Today we know that all the planets, including the Earth, move around the Sun in approximately circular orbits. Because Jupiter orbits the Sun outside the orbit of the Earth, it is called a superior planet. As seen from Earth, all superior planets appear to move eastward close to the ecliptic – the apparent yearly path of the Sun relative to the stars, which is the projection of the plane of the Earth's orbit, the ecliptic plane, against the stars.

In their solar orbits, planets move completely around the celestial sphere. Since Jupiter takes 11.86 Earth years to orbit the Sun, it also takes

this time to move around the star sphere. So, as viewed from Earth, Jupiter moves along the ecliptic year by year progressively entering each of the Zodiacal constellations, as noted by the ancient Babylonian writers of the *Enuma Elish*.

When a superior planet is directly opposite to the Sun in the sky it is in opposition (Figure 1-8). Earth is between the Sun and the planet which, at this time, shines its brightest in the southern sky at midnight in the northern hemisphere. The planet is closest to Earth, too. Jupiter comes into opposition every 13 months. Inferior planets – Mercury and Venus – cannot reach opposition because they are always within Earth's orbit. So they cannot appear in the midnight sky but remain relatively close to the Sun as seen from Earth.

8

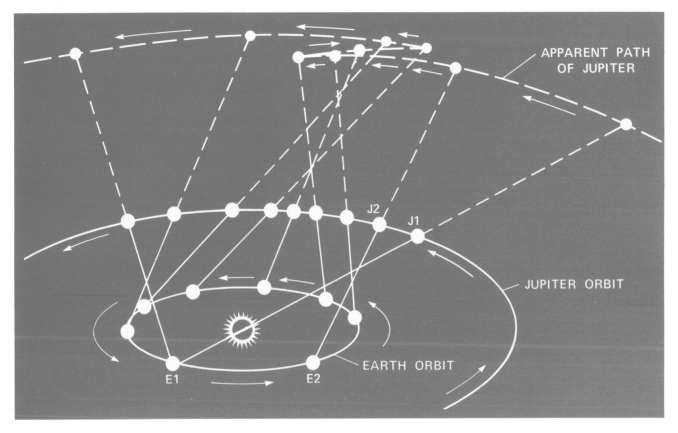

Figure 1-9. Because of the relative motions of Earth and Jupiter on their orbits, the Earth sometimes catches up with Jupiter since it moves faster. Then, as seen from Earth, Jupiter appears to move backwards through the sky for several months. A typical loop motion of Jupiter, as shown, covers about one-third of a Zodiacal constellation and was used by the Babylonians to trace 10 degrees in the sky.

Conjunction occurs when a planet is on the part of its orbit directly behind the Sun, as seen from Earth, and is thus not visible in the night sky. The planet is then most distant from Earth. This is referred to as superior conjunction to differentiate from inferior conjunction when a planet, orbiting within the Earth's orbit (i.e., Venus and Mercury), is between the Earth and Sun and is closest to Earth in its orbit.

Because the orbit of a superior planet is outside the orbit of the Earth, and because the Earth moves fastest, there is a period each year around the date of opposition when a superior planet is being overtaken and appears to move backward — toward the west — among the stars in what is termed retrograde motion (Figure 1-9).

Figure 1-10. Jupiter presents a magnificent colored globe in the best Earth-based photographs of the giant planet. The various belts and zones are clearly defined and the polar flattening is quite apparent. *(Photo: Catalina Observatory, University of Arizona)*

Jupiter the Planet

Jupiter measures 133,516 km (82,967 mi.) from pole to pole, compared with Earth's 12,900 km (8,000 mi.). Rotating faster than any other planet in the Solar System, Jupiter turns completely on its axis once in 9 hours 55-1/2 minutes. But the equatorial regions rotate slightly faster than other regions: in 9 hours 50-1/2 minutes. This means that any point on Jupiter's equator moves at 35,400 km (22,000 mi.) per hour compared with 1,600 km (1,000 mi.) per hour for a point on the Earth's equator.

As a consequence of the rapid rotation, the equatorial regions of Jupiter bulge outward under centripetal force to make the equatorial diameter of the visible globe about 9,280 km (5,767 mi.) greater than the polar diameter. Consequently, Jupiter (Figure 1-10) is not a sphere but has an

oblate shape, its polar diameter being 94.2 percent of its equatorial diameter. Earth is flattened at the poles but proportionately much less — to only 99.66 percent.

Although Jupiter's volume is 1317 times that of Earth, its mass is only just under 318 times Earth's mass. Since Jupiter is much less dense than Earth, it being only one and one-third times as dense as water, it cannot be a solid sphere like the Earth but instead must consist mainly of gas and liquid with possibly a small solid core. At least three-quarters of Jupiter probably consists of the lightest gases, hydrogen and helium; the same gases that are most common in the Sun and the stars. Jupiter is probably more like the Sun in basic composition than like the Earth.

The gases methane and ammonia have been detected in Jupiter's atmosphere and small

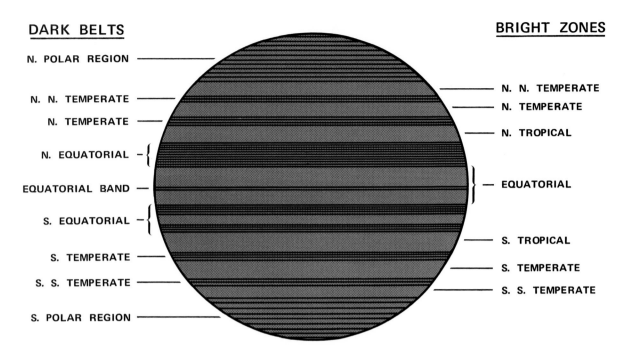

DARK BELTS

N. POLAR REGION

N. N. TEMPERATE

N. TEMPERATE

N. EQUATORIAL

EQUATORIAL BAND

S. EQUATORIAL

S. TEMPERATE

S. S. TEMPERATE

S. POLAR REGION

BRIGHT ZONES

N. N. TEMPERATE

N. TEMPERATE

N. TROPICAL

EQUATORIAL

S. TROPICAL

S. TEMPERATE

S. S. TEMPERATE

Figure 1-11. The belts and zones of Jupiter are permanent enough to be given the names shown here.

amounts of other gases such as ethane and acetylene. Other gases may be there but are difficult to detect in measurements made directly from Earth.

Seen through a telescope from Earth, Jupiter presents a magnificent sight, a striped banded disc of turbulent clouds with all the stripes parallel to the planet's equator. Large dusky gray regions cap each pole in an amorphous hood. Dark, brown or gray stripes are called belts; lighter, yellow-white colored bands between the belts are called zones. All the colors are soft, muted, but quite definite. Many of the belts and zones are permanent enough features to be given names (Figure 1-11).

Over the years, colors on Jupiter are observed to change; the zones vary from yellow to white, while the belts vary from gray to reddish brown. The bands fade and darken as well as change color. They may also widen or become narrow and move

up and down in latitude, i.e., farther from or closer to the equator.

Some astronomers suggest that the cold tops of the Jovian clouds in the zones consist of ammonia crystals and vapor. Water clouds are also likely but probably form at a level too deep in the atmosphere to be identified from Earth.

A transparent atmosphere rises some 50 to 65 km (30 to 40 mi.) above the cloud tops.

Many smaller features add interesting details to the zones and bands — streaks, wisps, arches, loops, plumes, patches, lumps, spots, festoons. Some are probably knots of clouds. These small features sometimes change form rapidly in the course of days or even of hours. The scale of Jupiter is so vast that even these features are thousands of miles in extent.

The cloud features of Jupiter move around the

11

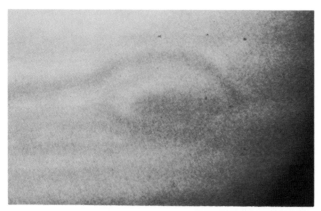

Figure 1-12. On the South Tropical Zone of Jupiter is a Great Red Spot which has intrigued astronomers for centuries. Speculation about the spot ranged from a floating island to a swirling column of gas anchored to some prominent feature on a solid core. *(Photo: Catalina Observatory)*

planet at different rates. For example, a great equatorial current sweeps around the planet at 360 km (225 mi.) per hour faster than regions on either side of it. It represents a 20 degree-wide girdle around the planet. In addition, some astronomers have interpreted observations as showing that the clouds move at different speeds at different altitudes.

In the southern hemisphere of Jupiter is an outstanding long oval feature known as the Great Red Spot (Figure 1-12). At present 24,000 km (15,000 mi.) long, it has at times extended almost 48,000 km (30,000 mi.). The spot has intrigued generations of astronomers since first observed and recorded centuries ago. In 1664, during the reign of Charles II, the astronomer Robert Hooke reported seeing a large red spot on Jupiter, which could have been the first observation of the Great Red Spot. This was, indeed, the first record of a scientific discovery from a government research contract. In 1665, Cassini referred to the marking as the "Eye of Jupiter." The spot appeared and vanished at least eight times between the years 1665 and 1708, and became a strikingly conspicuous red object in 1878. Early in 1883, the Great

Red Spot faded to become almost invisible and then became distinct again, only to fade once more at the beginning of the present century.

The spot was likened to something floating in the atmosphere of Jupiter; early astronomers suggested that it was a raft or an island, since over the centuries the spot drifted around the planet relative to the average movement of the clouds. Sometimes cloud currents have swept around it as though the spot itself were a vortex in the atmosphere. Some scientists postulated that the Great Red Spot represents a column of gas, the center of an enormous whirlpool-like mass of gas rising from deep in the planet to the top of the atmosphere and anchored in some way to the surface far below.

That the Great Red Spot is a hurricane-like structure — a fantastic grouping of "thunderstorms" — was suggested from recent astronomical investigations prior to the Pioneer mission to Jupiter. Photographs to detect methane revealed that the Great Red Spot is the highest cloud structure on Jupiter and thus implied that the marking might have some internal energy source to push it above the other cloud layers. This would be unlikely if it were a floating mass such as an island, but could be explained by its consisting of a large grouping of thunderstorms — rising air masses.

On Jupiter there are also white spots which are more short lived than the Great Red Spot. They seem to be atmospheric storms, too, and become quite bright for relatively short periods of time (Figure 1-13). These white spots also move relative to the nearby cloud systems.

Jupiter emits three different types of radio waves. These are not like the signals that carry programs on Earth radios but are more akin to the sferics (static or "noise") that interfere with a program when lightning flashes or electric motors are run nearby. The radio noise reaching Earth from Jupiter is greater than that from any other extraterrestrial source except the Sun. The three types are called thermal, decimetric, and decametric radiation.

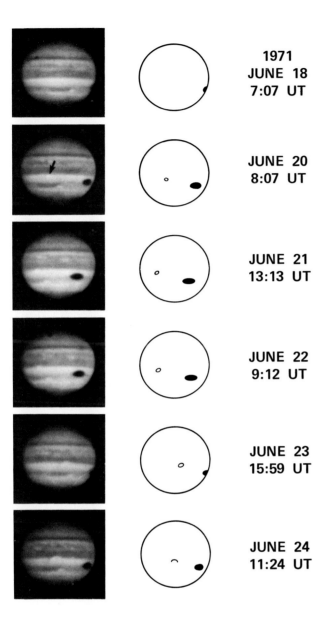

The thermal radiation is at wavelengths less than a few centimeters. Decimetric radio waves are from a few centimeters to tens of centimeters in length. Decametric refers to radio waves with wavelengths of tens of meters (Figure 1-14).

Thermal radio waves are produced by molecules moving about in the atmosphere of Jupiter. Decimetric radio waves are produced by electrons moving about — oscillating — above the atmosphere. Decametric radio waves are produced by electrical discharges, like lightning flashes, in the upper atmosphere of Jupiter.

	1971 JUNE 18 7:07 UT
	JUNE 20 8:07 UT
	JUNE 21 13:13 UT
	JUNE 22 9:12 UT
	JUNE 23 15:59 UT
	JUNE 24 11:24 UT

Figure 1-13. Jupiter often exhibits temporary white spots which suddenly appear, become bright then fade away. This set of ultraviolet photographs from the International Planetary Patrol Program shows the spectacular early growth of a major disturbance in the South Equatorial Belt of Jupiter. North is at the top. The event started as a tiny spot barely detectable in ultraviolet light on June 18 and spread to a size comparable with the Red Spot in less than a week. It is identified (at an age of two days) by the arrow on the image of June 20, where it stands out very clearly. At that time the disturbance was not yet detectable in red photographs of comparable quality. The images in this particular set were obtained at the Mauna Kea Observatory and the Perth Observatory.

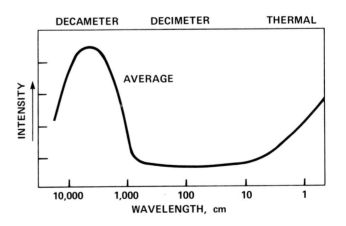

Figure 1-14. Jupiter emits radio waves which have been recorded and measured by radio astronomers for several decades. They are of three main types: thermal, decimetric and decametric. Each has a different origin.

13

Scientists observed that the decametric radio signals from Jupiter appeared to be linked in some mysterious way to the orbital motion of Jupiter's closest big satellite, Io. Bursts of electrical energy, somehow triggered by Io, are equivalent to billions of simultaneous lightning flashes on Earth.

Observations of the decimetric radio waves from Jupiter caused scientists to conclude that the planet possesses radiation belts similar to those of Earth in which charged particles are trapped and move under the influence of an intense magnetic field. From the intensity of the radiation it was also concluded that Jupiter's magnetic field must be many times stronger than Earth's field. Thus Jupiter and the Earth are the only two planets of the Solar System known to have strong magnetic fields.

The magnetic field of Jupiter traps protons (nuclei of hydrogen atoms) and electrons that flow through interplanetary space from the Sun and are referred to as the solar wind. These trapped, electrically charged particles move backward and forward across the equator of the planet, forming radiation belts.

The electrons, oscillating along the lines of force of the magnetic field, generate radio waves in a similar fashion to electrons caused to oscillate within the antenna of a radio transmitter.

Jupiter is internally quite different from the inner planets (Figure 1-15).

Astronomers generally agree to a basic internal structure of Jupiter, although they differ in detail and interpretation. The average temperature on the top of the cloud layer is very low by terrestrial standards, probably about 150 degrees Kelvin (−189° F). Below the cloud tops the temperature rises steadily. The topmost regions consist of supercold ammonia crystals, ammonia droplets, and ammonia vapor. As temperature rises with depth into the atmosphere, there may be ice crystals, water droplets, and water vapor present. Estimates of the total depth of the Jovian atmosphere vary enormously, from 95 to 5,800 km (60 to 3,600 mi.) before a "surface" would be reached. This "surface," however, may be a gradual transition from gaseous to liquid hydrogen rather than a sharp interface between gas and liquid or a solid surface. Modern theories suggest a very deep atmosphere at the bottom of which the pressure, exerted by the weight of all the gas above, is enormous, reaching millions of times Earth's 14 pounds per square inch sea level pressure.

Such great pressure could convert hydrogen into a special form in which it behaves like a metal: it readily conducts both heat and electricity as metals do. So beneath a sea of liquid hydrogen could be a shell of metallic hydrogen (probably liquid because of the high temperature) surrounding a small internal core consisting of rocky material and other metals; somewhat the same as the composition of the inner planets, including the Earth. Jupiter's core has been estimated as ten times the mass of the Earth. However, the existence of such a rocky core is still widely debated among planetologists.

Near the center of Jupiter, the temperature might be tens of thousands of degrees and could account for Jupiter radiating into space 2.3 times as much energy as the planet receives from the Sun.

Planetary Evolution

Planets of the Solar System probably formed four to five billion years ago when hosts of small rocky particles and clouds of gas were drawn together by their own gravity. It is believed that after the Sun itself condensed from a primordial nebula, planets of different sizes formed from different concentrations of matter present at various distances from the Sun. Electrical and magnetic forces in the gas clouds or gravitational collapse of the proto solar cloud probably thrust the condensing planets into orbits around the central Sun. Those planets that started to aggregate early scooped up more matter than those which started later and had less free material to collect. Mass distribution in the cloud probably had a lot to do with the resultant masses of the planets.

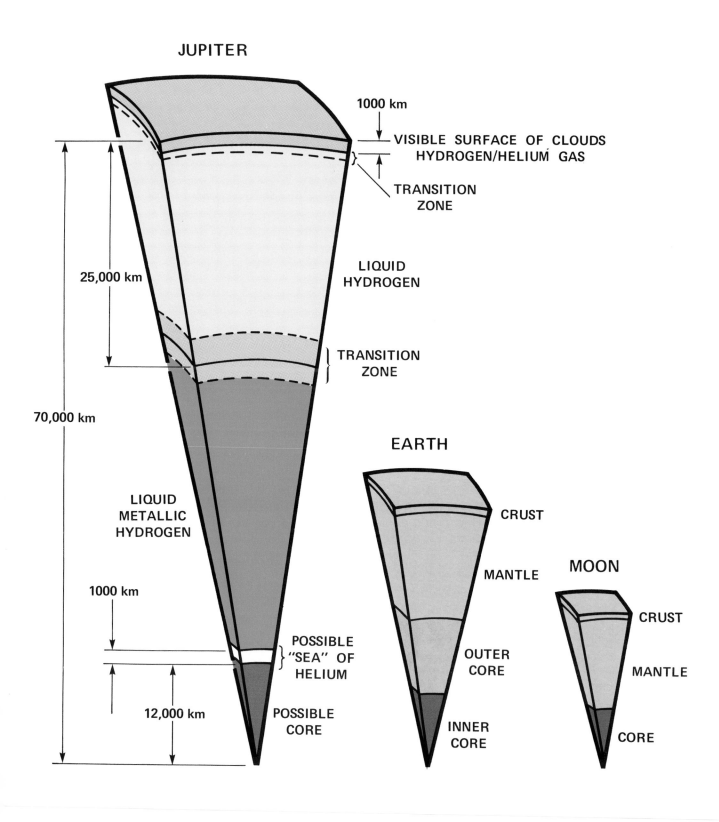

JUPITER

1000 km

VISIBLE SURFACE OF CLOUDS
HYDROGEN/HELIUM GAS

TRANSITION ZONE

25,000 km

LIQUID HYDROGEN

TRANSITION ZONE

70,000 km

EARTH

LIQUID METALLIC HYDROGEN

CRUST

MANTLE

MOON

1000 km

CRUST

POSSIBLE "SEA" OF HELIUM

OUTER CORE

MANTLE

12,000 km

POSSIBLE CORE

INNER CORE

CORE

Figure 1-15. The interior of Jupiter is quite different from the interiors of terrestrial planets such as Earth and Moon.

(a)

(b)

(c)

Scientific experiments made by space probes that photographed the inner planets and their satellites, coupled with geological evidence on Earth and radar probing to the surface of Venus, indicate that the terrestrial planets have been highly cratered, and this cratering presents evidence of the final stages of planetary accretion (Figure 1-16). On Earth, subsequent changes to the surface through internal heat, plate tectonics, and weathering obliterated nearly all evidence of impact cratering.

Much of the primordial gas was hydrogen — the most common material in the universe — which consists of a proton and an orbital electron. The Sun, for example, is nearly all hydrogen, as are the stars. Astronomers have also discovered vast clouds of hydrogen in the spaces between the stars.

While it is most probable that the Earth and the other inner planets were never able to attract much hydrogen, they may have possessed some hydrogen in their atmospheres for a relatively short time on the scale of planetary development. Hydrogen atmospheres of the inner planets could have been lost by massive eruptions on the Sun during its early development. Also, the closeness of the terrestrial type planets to the Sun, coupled with their

Figure 1-16. The planets are believed to have accreted from particles that condensed form a primordial solar nebula. Evidence of the final stages of accretion is believed to be the impact craters on the terrestrial planets.

(a) Mercury – Crater Kuiper (Mariner 10)
(b) Earth – Meteor Crater, Arizona (Photo USGS)
(c) Moon – Clavius (Hale Observatories)
(d) Mars – Unnamed large crater with crater comparable to Earth's Meteor Crater below and slightly to left.

16

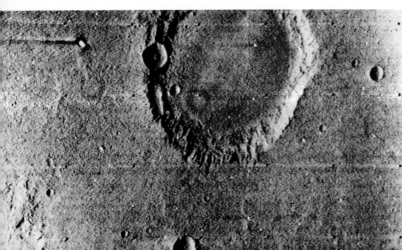

(d)

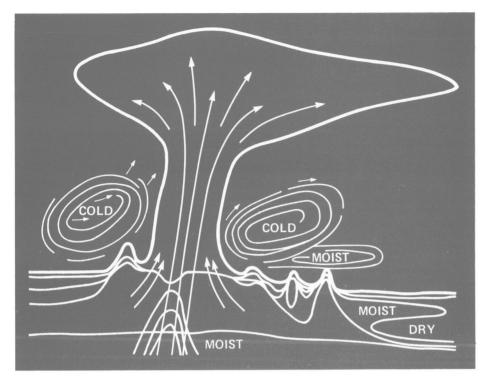

Figure 1-17. Heat in an atmosphere drives rising masses of air which on Earth produce thunderstorms. As the air cools in the upper atmosphere it spreads sideways and rotation of the planet causes swirling motions. Internal heat on Jupiter may be producing huge groups of thunderstorms which appear as spots such as the Great Red Spot.

relatively small gravities, allowed hydrogen to escape into space. But the cooler Jupiter, 565 million km (350 million mi.) beyond Mars, with additionally a much stronger gravity, holds hydrogen in tremendous quantities. So probably do the other large planets: Saturn, Uranus, and Neptune.

Knowledge about these complex atmospheres may help our understanding of Earth's more simple atmosphere. Already the study of dust storms in Mars' very thin, dry atmosphere, and the circulation patterns in Venus' very dense atmosphere, is helping meteorologists understand the dynamics of planetary atmospheres in general.

At some level in the deep atmosphere of Jupiter the temperature should equal that on Earth. At this level ammonia crystals could become liquid ammonia droplets. Water could condense too. Such

droplets could rain from the clouds, sometimes frozen into snows of water and ammonia. But the drops and snowflakes could never fall to the surface as they do on Earth. Instead, at warm lower regions of the deep atmosphere, they would probably evaporate and rise back into the clouds.

Such a circulation pattern, somewhat analogous to those that build up violent thunderstorms and tornadoes in Earth's atmosphere (Figure 1-17), would probably give rise to endless violent turbulence in the Jovian atmosphere; more violent by far than the thunderstorms of Earth. Accompanying electrical discharges would probably make Earth's lightning flashes mere sparks by comparison. Thus, vertical movements in the atmosphere of Jupiter may provide examples of the most violent storms imaginable. At the same time jet circulations in the

17

cloud bands and zones may be analogous to Earth's major atmospheric patterns such as the trade winds, tropical convergences and jet streams.

At first thought Jupiter might be considered an inhospitable planet on which life could not survive. This need not necessarily be so. Since there are probably liquid water droplets in an atmosphere of hydrogen, methane and ammonia, Jupiter may provide the same kind of primordial "soup" in which scientists currently believe that life originated on Earth.

Life has been described as an unexplained ability to organize inanimate matter into a living system that perceives, reacts to, and evolves to cope with changes to the physical environment that threaten to destroy its organization. In 1953, a mixture of hydrogen, methane, ammonia, and water vapor — the kind of atmosphere Jupiter still retains today

and many scientists believe Earth possessed soon after its formation — was bombarded in a laboratory with electrical discharges. These were passed through the gas mixture to simulate the effects of bolts of lightning. The electrical energy bound together some of the simple gas molecules into more complex molecules of carbon, hydrogen, nitrogen, and oxygen of the type believed to be the building blocks for living systems (Figure 1-18).

Figure 1-18. By passing electrical sparks through mixtures of hydrogen, methane, ammonia, and water vapor, scientists produced colored amino acids, the building blocks of organic life. The experiment was first performed by Stanley Miller in 1953 and has now been repeated many times elsewhere. These photographs show an experiment at NASA-Ames Research Center's Chemical Evolution Branch. When methane or acetylene, both constituents of the Jovian atmosphere, is sparked in a chamber together with ammonia at the temperature of liquid nitrogen, reddish-brown polymeric material is synthesized. Such processes might be responsible for the colors of the Jovian atmosphere.

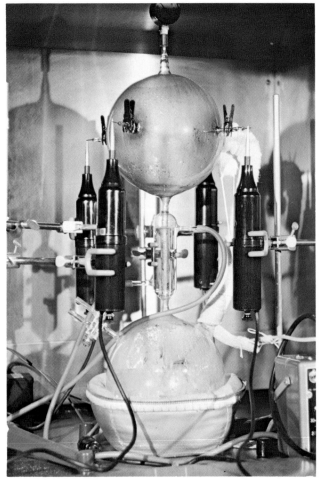

(a)

(b)

At some point in Earth's history, postulated at about 3.5 billion years ago, something organized the complex carbon-based molecules of Earth's oceans and atmosphere into living systems which were then able to make copies of themselves — to reproduce. It is theorized that from then on, by slight changes to subsequent copies, biological evolution produced all the living creatures of Earth, including Man.

The big question is: Has life evolved in the atmosphere of Jupiter? It is known that the temperature may be right at lower elevations in the Jovian atmosphere. It is known that the gas mixture may be suitable. It is known that electrical discharges probably take place. Jupiter could hold a key to the evolution of life, and this key may be found if unmanned probes are sent to the Jovian atmosphere later this century. Such probes are technologically possible today as a result of experience gained with the Pioneer flyby of Jupiter and probes to other planets.

Mission Objectives

Why a mission to Jupiter?

The question of beginnings has always intrigued mankind. How did something appear from nothing and become the physical universe? Man is still far from having satisfactory answers even as to how the Solar System condensed from charged atoms, energetic molecules, and electromagnetic forces of some primeval nebula. How did the various planets evolve their unique differences? How did life originate and flourish on Earth, a planet so different from all the others?

It is not easy to find answers here on Earth since this planet can be studied only in its present stage of evolution, a single frame in the long motion picture of Earth's history as an astronomical body. The single picture does not provide enough information for scientists to be really sure about Earth's past let alone its future. However, other planets may pass through evolutionary history at different rates, and some, such as the Moon and Mercury,

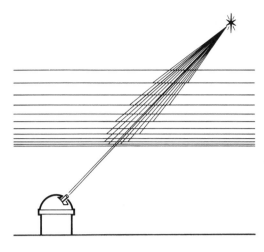

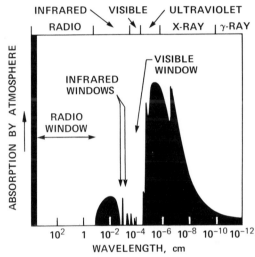

Figure 1-19. Because the Earth's atmosphere selectively absorbs certain wavelengths of light, especially in the infrared and the ultraviolet regions of the spectrum, astronomers obtain only a partial view of planets from the Earth.

have "fossilized" so that they preserve the ancient record of planetary evolution.

It is not possible to study planets in very great detail by use of telescopes on Earth; all the planets are much too far away and, in addition, observations are limited by the screening and distorting effects of the Earth's atmosphere (Figure 1-19). Since planetary probes have been dispatched, astronomers have undoubtedly learned more about the planets during the last ten years than in all the previous centuries of observation from Earth.

Knowledge about these other planets is important to our understanding of our own planet, its

19

Figure 1-20. The planet Saturn will be visited by Pioneer 11 in 1979 and later by a more advanced spacecraft, Mariner Jupiter-Saturn. (*Photo.: Catalina Observatory, University of Arizona*)

past and its future. Such knowledge and understanding might be vital to the long-term survival of the human species if people are to adapt to inevitable natural and man-caused changes to the Earth's environment. Mankind might be able to predict long-term changes to the terrestrial environment and prepare for them.

In many respects, Jupiter provides a model of what is taking place in the universe at large. Many processes on Jupiter may be similar to those in stars before their nuclear reactions begin. And the great turmoil in Jupiter's processes, coupled with the high speed of planetary rotation, provides an extreme model for the study of jet streams and weather in quieter planetary atmospheres such as the Earth's.

The satellites of Jupiter represent a veritable Solar System in miniature, even to the densities of the satellites, like the planets, decreasing with distance from the central body. Thus, their for-

mation may have paralleled the formation of the Solar System. Astronomers are questioning whether these satellites are Earth-like planetary bodies, or more like giant snowballs. The four outermost satellites, Andrastea, Pan, Poseidon, and Hades, move around Jupiter in a counter direction to most of the Jovian satellites. They could be captured asteroids. Examination of the surfaces of the Jovian satellites by space probes may reveal differences that will throw light upon their origin. So far only the four large Jovian satellites have been seen at close hand, as described later in this book.

The outer Solar System is relatively unknown to Man. Saturn (Figure 1-20), the next planet beyond Jupiter, never approaches closer than 1250 million km (780 million mi.) of Earth; while Uranus, the next planet, is almost one billion miles farther away.

Saturn will not be reached by a spacecraft until Pioneer 11 flies by it in September 1979.

20

Figure 1-21. The gravity of Jupiter, coupled with the planet's orbital motion, can be used in a slingshot technique to speed spacecraft to the outer planets. But first NASA had to find out if the environment of Jupiter could be penetrated without causing the spacecraft to fail.

Yet these big planets of the Solar System are probably of great importance to developing a full understanding of the system's origin. Since they are so distant, they require that spacecraft travel very fast to reach them in reasonable times. Unfortunately, launch vehicles cannot boost spacecraft of practical size to the necessary high velocities. However, by using the gravitational field and orbital motion of Jupiter in a slingshot technique, spacecraft can be swung into more energetic paths to carry them relatively quickly to the outer planets (Figure 1-21).

Jupiter thus provides a means to explore the outer Solar System. But there is a problem: Jupiter's strong magnetic field traps charged particles in radiation belts that extend out from the planet a greater distance than from Earth to Moon. Without exploring these radiation belts, scientists could not be sure the belts would not damage any spacecraft using Jupiter as a gravity slingshot to the outer

planets. If the radiation belts proved to be a serious hazard, the exploration of the outer Solar System might have to wait until more energetic propulsion systems than chemical rockets could be developed, perhaps several decades hence.

Although scientists can tell from the radio waves emitted by the Jovian radiation belts approximately how many electrons are trapped in the belts, they have no way of knowing from Earth how many high energy protons are trapped there, and it is especially the protons that do the damage. The only way to find out is to send a spacecraft to Jupiter to penetrate the radiation belts and measure the protons on the spot and this has been done by the two Pioneers.

Such a mission to Jupiter poses many technical challenges. It extends Man's exploration of the Solar System to a new scale — 800 million km (half a billion mi.) to Jupiter compared with only 65 million km (40 million mi.) to Mars. The vast

21

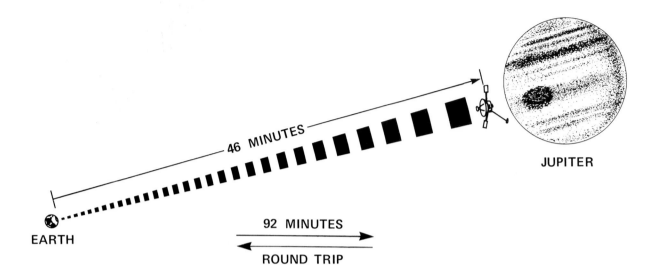

46 MINUTES

EARTH

JUPITER

92 MINUTES

ROUND TRIP

Figure 1-22. A problem with visiting the outer planets is the long time needed for radio waves, traveling at 300,000 km (186,000 miles) per second, to travel between Earth and the spacecraft; this time is 92 minutes for the round trip by radio from Earth to Jupiter and back.

distance presents problems of communications; not only the diminution of the radio signals, but also the time delay in information traveling to Earth from the spacecraft and the equal time delay for radio commands from Earth to reach the spacecraft (Figure 1-22). This delay makes it necessary for controllers on Earth to become skilled in flying the spacecraft 90 minutes out of step with the spacecraft itself at the distance of Jupiter. Everything has to be planned well in advance with no opportunity to react to and correct for any hazards caused by unknowns.

SUN AS SEEN
FROM EARTH

SUN AS SEEN
FROM JUPITER

Figure 1-23. Converting solar power to electrical energy is not practical for small spacecraft at the distance of Jupiter where sunlight carries only one twenty-seventh the energy it does at Earth.

Additionally, because of the great distance traveled from the Sun itself, the sunlight at the distance of Jupiter has an intensity of only one twenty-seventh of that at Earth's distance from the Sun (Figure 1-23). The normal method of supplying electrical power in space by converting sunlight to electricity cannot be used. A spacecraft bound for Jupiter has to carry a nuclear energy source to generate electricity. Also the spacecraft must fly through space for several years before reaching its objective. So new levels of high reliability are mandatory. Moreover, the high velocities needed to reach Jupiter call for a lightweight spacecraft, thereby demanding lightweight design of the spacecraft and all its components and scientific instruments.

Finally, between Mars and Jupiter is the asteroid belt (Figure 1-24), which some theories suggested may be a 280-million-km (175-million-mi.) wide zone of abrasive dust that might seriously damage any spacecraft trying to cross it.

Figure 1-24. Between Mars and Jupiter lies the asteroid belt, which spacecraft must cross if they are to visit the outer solar system. The big question faced was how dangerous would this asteroid belt be to such spacecraft?

Such were the obstacles. But the opportunity to explore the outer Solar System beyond the orbit of Mars beckons strongly, challenging the ingenuity of space technologists. The National Aeronautics and Space Administration accepted the challenge in a double-pronged exploratory program: two spacecraft, Pioneers F and G, were planned to make the assault on Jupiter. Their mission was a journey into the unknown territory of space, truly a pioneer odyssey for an encounter with a giant to open the outer Solar System for mankind. Thus began to unfold early in 1970, the story of an incredible journey to the planet Jupiter and beyond; a mission to the most spectacular object in the night skies of Earth, an object that has not only held the attention of mankind since time immemorial, but also offers a doorway to the outer Solar System.

23

24

2
The Pioneer Jupiter Mission

A scientific paper by H. F. Matthews and Charles F. Hall delivered to the American Astronautical Society's June 1969 meeting in Denver, Colorado, described the first mission to the outer planets. "An exciting era of exploration of the outer planets has been initiated by NASA in recently approving the Pioneer F/G mission for flights to Jupiter in 1972 and in 1973."

Preceding years had seen a number of proposals and scientific papers about exploration of the outer planets, including missions to visit several planets by one spacecraft using gravity assist from other planets. Several NASA centers and private industry had completed studies showing that the gravity field of Jupiter combined with the orbital motion of the planet could accelerate spacecraft to speeds at which they could complete missions to more distant planets in reasonable times with useful payloads.

In March 1967, for example, a paper presented at the Fifth Goddard Memorial Symposium in Washington, D. C., discussed several types of galactic Jupiter probes aimed at exploring the interplanetary space beyond Mars, the solar wind and its interaction with deep space, and the environment of Jupiter. The paper pointed out, too, that such a Jupiter probe would be accelerated by the large planet sufficiently for the spacecraft to escape completely from the Solar System and cruise into interstellar space.

Official approval of a mission to Jupiter came from NASA in February 1969, and it was assigned to the Planetary Program Office, Office of Space Science and Applications. NASA selected the Pioneer Project Office at Ames Research Center, Moffett Field, Mountain View, California, to manage the Jupiter project, and TRW Systems Group, Redondo Beach, California, as the contractor to design and fabricate two identical Pioneer spacecraft for this new mission.

Relative positions of Earth and Jupiter on their orbits permit a spacecraft to be launched to Jupiter every 13 months with minimum launch energy. The first opportunity that seemed feasible for the Pioneer mission, taking into consideration the time needed to build the spacecraft, select its scientific experiments and build instruments to perform them, appeared to be the 1972 opportunity extending from late February through early March. NASA scheduled the first spacecraft, Pioneer F, to meet this launch window. A second spacecraft, Pioneer G, was planned for launching approximately 13 months later during the 1973 opportunity.

Planning

Planning for the Pioneer mission to Jupiter involved organizations within NASA and industry. The Pioneer Program was managed at NASA Headquarters, originally by Glenn A. Reiff and later by F. D. Kochendorfer.

At NASA-Ames Research Center, Charles F. Hall became manager of the Pioneer Project. The experiments system of the spacecraft became the responsibility of Joseph E. Lepetich, and the spacecraft system, that of Ralph W. Holtzclaw. The flight operations manager was originally Robert R. Nunamaker and later Norman J. Martin. Dr. John H. Wolfe became project scientist; Robert U. Hofstetter, launch vehicle and trajectory analysis coordinator; Richard O. Fimmel, science chief; and Gilbert A. Schroeder, spacecraft chief.

The Jet Propulsion Laboratory of California Institute of Technology, Pasadena, California, provided tracking and data system support with originally A. J. Siegmeth and later Richard B. Miller, manager of the Deep Space Network for Pioneer, NASA-Goddard Spaceflight Center, Greenbelt, Maryland, provided the worldwide communications.

The launch vehicle system became the responsibility of NASA's Lewis Research Center, Cleveland, Ohio, under management of D. J. Shramo. Launch operations were the responsibility of NASA's John F. Kennedy Space Center, Florida, where the representative for the Pioneer Jupiter project was J. W. Johnson.

At TRW Systems Group, B. J. O'Brien managed the Pioneer Jupiter project. At the Atomic Energy Commission, B. Rock became project engineer for the SNAP-19 radioisotope thermonuclear power generators to be built by Teledyne Isotopes. Bendix Field Engineering Corporation, under the management of Walter L. Natzic, supported the mission operations system. As appropriate, these responsibilities are, of course, continued into the mission beyond Jupiter until communication is lost with the spacecraft nearly a decade after launching.

Objectives of the Pioneer Jupiter mission were early defined by NASA as:

★ Explore the interplanetary medium beyond the orbit of Mars.

★ Investigate the nature of the asteroid belt from the scientific standpoint and assess the belt's possible hazard to missions to the outer planets.

★ Explore the environment of Jupiter.

26

Figure 2-1. The Jupiter mission needed the highest-yet launch velocity of a spacecraft, actually the highest velocity of any man-made object, over 51,500 km (32,000 miles) per hour. This was achieved with an Atlas-Centaur to which was added a third upper stage.

Ames Research Center was chosen for the mission because of previous experience with earlier spin-stabilized spacecraft that are still exploring the inner Solar System on a continuing basis. The new Pioneer was required to utilize proven spacecraft modules of Pioneers 6 through 9 to produce a small, lightweight, magnetically clean, interplanetary spacecraft.

To propel the 550-pound spacecraft to the unprecedented velocity needed to enter a transfer trajectory to Jupiter, the Atlas-Centaur launch vehicle (Figure 2-1) was equipped with an additional solid-propellant third stage.

Scientific experiments were selected over a series of planning meetings in the late 1960's, and by early 1970, all science experiments had been settled: measurements of magnetic fields; measurement of plasma; Zodiacal Light measurements; polarimetry and imaging of Jupiter and several Jovian satellites; determination of composition of charged particles; recording of cosmic rays; ultraviolet and infrared observations of Jupiter; and detecting asteroids and meteoroids. In addition, as with other spacecraft, the radio communications signal would provide a probe into the atmosphere of the planet as the spacecraft passed behind it, and tracking data from the signal would provide information about the mass of Jupiter and its satellites. Principal investigators were appointed for all the experiments, and contracts were awarded to build the instruments and conduct the experiments. All experiments are described more fully in Chapter 4.

Mission Overview

The two spacecraft for this mission were identical. The first, Pioneer F, blazed the trail; had the environment of the asteroid belt or of Jupiter caused a failure, the second spacecraft, Pioneer G, would have provided a backup. Initially, Pioneer G was launched and targeted to follow the path of Pioneer F. However, the capability existed and, therefore, it was planned that Pioneer G be retargeted as necessary, based upon the results from the first spacecraft's encounter with Jupiter. And this was done.

The launch vehicle boosted the spacecraft in direct ascent, i.e., with no parking orbit, to start the flight to Jupiter at about 51,500 km (32,000 mi.) per hour. A trip of just under 600 days was the shortest time to Jupiter within the capabilities of the launch vehicle, and a trip of 748 days, the longest.

In-flight maneuvers were planned to take place several times during the mission to target the spacecraft to arrive at Jupiter at a time and position suitable for best observing the planet and several of its large satellites.

Design requirements were established for each spacecraft to mate physically with the launch vehicle, and for its communications system to be compatible with the Deep Space Network. Each Pioneer had also to provide a thermally controlled environment for scientific instruments.

The Pioneer spacecraft must operate reliably in space for many years (Figure 2-2). Each carries a data system to sample the scientific instruments and to transmit scientific and engineering information about the "health" of the spacecraft and its instruments over the vast distances to Earth. The spacecraft also have to be capable of being commanded from Earth to perform their mission and

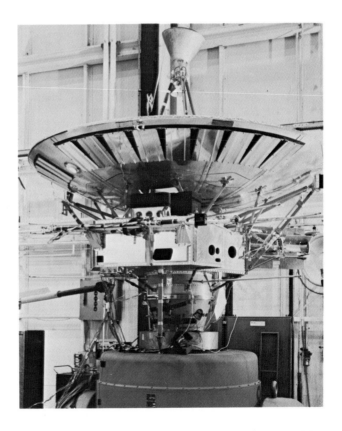

Figure 2-2. The Pioneer spacecraft itself was designed for high reliability using space-proven components. TRW Systems designed and fabricated the two Jupiter spacecraft, Pioneers F and G, at their Redondo Beach, California, facility.

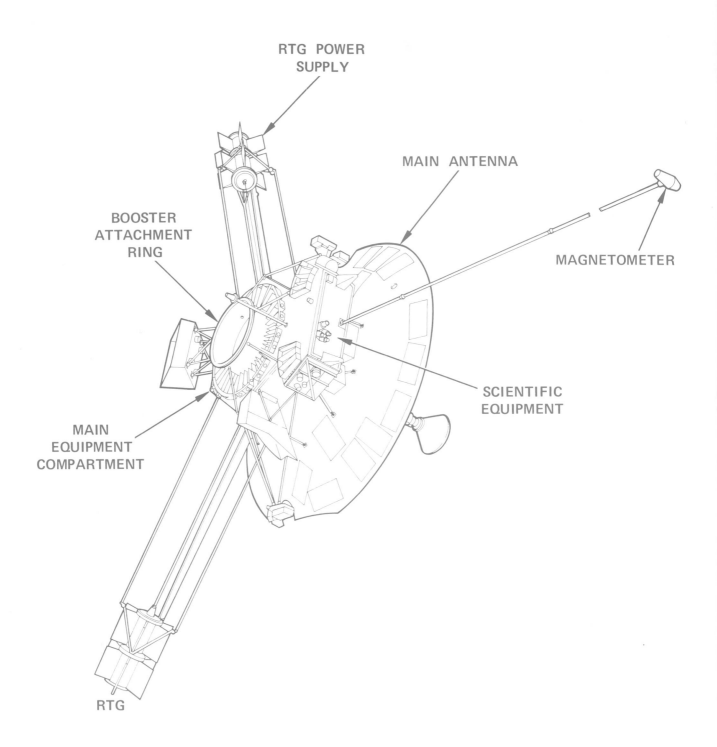

RTG POWER
SUPPLY

MAIN ANTENNA

BOOSTER
ATTACHMENT
RING

MAGNETOMETER

SCIENTIFIC
EQUIPMENT

MAIN
EQUIPMENT
COMPARTMENT

RTG

Figure 2-3. Each spacecraft was spin stabilized in flight, and carried a large antenna for communications and a number of scientific instruments.

to change the operating modes of equipment aboard them (Figure 2-3).

Each Pioneer's curved path to Jupiter is some 1000 million km (620 million mi.) long, covering about 160 degrees azimuthly around the Sun between the orbits of Earth and Jupiter. During Pioneer's flight from Earth to Jupiter, Earth travels almost twice around the Sun while Jupiter moves only about one sixth of the way around its solar orbit.

There were options on the path to Jupiter. Some arrival dates were forbidden because the sensors would not have been able to perform the scientific experiments desired; others because they would have clashed with the arrival of another spacecraft, Mariner 10, at Venus or Mercury and given rise to conflicting requirements for the use of the big 64-meter (210-foot) antennas of the Deep Space Network.

Launch windows were available for Pioneer F from February 25 to March 20, 1972, with arrival at Jupiter between the middle of October 1973 and late July 1974. Arrival had to be timed so that Jupiter and the spacecraft would not appear too close to the Sun as observed from Earth. Approximately 300 to 325 days and 700 to 725 days after launch, the motions of Earth and the spacecraft put them on opposite sides of the Sun. Thus arrival at Jupiter beyond 700 days after launch would have been impractical. The earlier passage of the spacecraft behind the Sun, just over 300 days after launch, interrupted communication with Pioneer 10 but not at a critical period of the mission. There were similar options for Pioneer G one year later.

There were also targeting options at Jupiter itself, such as how close the spacecraft should be allowed to approach the planet, how the trajectory should be inclined to the equatorial plane of Jupiter, and the position of the closest approach relative to the equatorial plane of Jupiter.

Early in planning the program, a decision was made that the encounter trajectory (Figure 2-4) for Pioneer F should be one that would provide maxi-

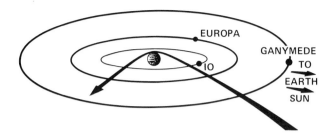

Figure 2-4. The first encounter trajectory with Jupiter was chosen to probe into the radiation belts and ensure that the spacecraft would have opportunities to obtain images of the terminator, the Great Red Spot, and several satellites, and would go into occultation behind Io as seen from Earth.

mum information about the radiation environment, even if this damaged the spacecraft and ended the mission at Jupiter. Hence, imaging of Jupiter could only be ensured before closest approach. An approach trajectory was, therefore, selected to present a well-illuminated planet for the pre-encounter phase, and a partially illuminated (crescent) planet as seen from the spacecraft after encounter. Although at first it seemed desirable that occultation of the spacecraft should be avoided, an occultation was selected since it could provide useful information about the atmosphere of Jupiter unobtainable in any other way.

Because Jupiter has radiation belts trapped by its magnetic field, the question of how close a spacecraft can approach Jupiter to take advantage of the gravity slingshot effect without damage to its electronic and optical equipment needed to be answered. This was one of several primary objectives of the first Pioneer fly-by mission.

In July 1971, scientists held a workshop at the Jet Propulsion Laboratory to define the environment of Jupiter in terms of the best information available at that date. With slight modifications, this environment was accepted as a design environment for the Pioneer Jupiter mission, for the spacecraft, and for its scientific instruments. But no one could be sure that the environment, although based on the very best observations from Earth, was the true environment of Jupiter. One Pioneer task was to determine this true environment.

There was, of course, a trade-off to a certain extent in that although approaching closer would increase the intensity of radiation, the spacecraft would fly by Jupiter more quickly and, thus, be exposed to the radiation for a shorter time. These two factors, which determine the integrated or total radiation dosage, were carefully weighed in the light of known information about Jupiter.

In general, the mission was designed to fly by Jupiter at three times the radius of the planet (referred to as $3R_J$), i.e., twice the radius of Jupiter above the cloud tops, not because the spacecraft could not be targeted to go closer, but rather because available information suggested this was the closest a spacecraft might approach without damage by radiation. At the time of mission planning, the ephemeris of Jupiter was uncertain to about 2000 km (1250 mi.), but navigationally, the spacecraft could have been sent within 3/8 Jupiter radii above the surface. Navigation to Jupiter is simplified somewhat because the massive gravity of the planet provides a focusing effect. An error in aiming by 1600 km (1000 mi.) would be narrowed to only 480 km (300 mi.) by this gravity focusing. But the error in the time of arrival is magnified by the same effect.

The choice of approach having been made, the scientific instruments were designed to survive the expected radiation intensities for the period that Pioneer F would be within the radiation belts.

Time of arrival at Jupiter could be changed by several days with the amount of propellant carried by the spacecraft, and this made it possible to fly close to a satellite for imaging, or to be occulted by a satellite.

Mission Hazards

In 1800, Johann Elert Bode called a meeting of astronomers at the observatory of Schröter in Lilienthal, Germany. He asked these astronomers to search for an undiscovered planet believed to be orbiting between Mars and Jupiter. On January 1, 1801, Giuseppe Piazzi, director of the Observatory of Palermo, Italy, discovered such a small planetary object, 1022 km (635 mi.) in diameter, which he named Ceres. But soon after its discovery, Ceres moved along its orbit into the glare of the Sun and was lost.

The great mathematician, Gauss, then developed the theory for orbit determination from a minimum number of observations and calculated the small planet's orbit and showed where it might be found again as it emerged from the solar glare. While observing Ceres again in 1802, Olbers discovered a second planetary body which he named Pallas. It was even smaller than Ceres; only 560 km (348 mi.) across. Astronomers were even more surprised when Harding discovered 226-km (141-mi.) diameter Juno in 1804, and Olbers found 504-km (313 mi.) Vesta — actually the brightest of these minor planets — in 1807. These diminutive planetary bodies (Figure 2-5) were termed asteroids by Herschel. They were regarded as fragments of a trans-Martian planet.

Today it is known that there are at least eight other asteroids larger than Juno but they were not found until half a century after the discovery of the first four of these bodies. Then the year 1845 saw the beginning of discoveries of many minor planets until today between 40,000 and 100,000 are postulated. Many have been discovered photographically (Figure 2-6). While most are between the orbits of Mars and Jupiter, other stray closer to and farther from the Sun in elliptical orbits. Several have approached Earth; one at least approaches the orbit of Mercury, and another that of Saturn (Figure 2-7). All are relatively small objects on the planetary scale.

While the orbits of the larger asteroids are cataloged, there are many asteroids whose orbits are unknown. The risk of Pioneer colliding with any of the charted asteroids was negligible. But there was no way of knowing how many sand-grain-sized particles might be there to impact on the spacecraft and lead to serious damage.

At the time of the program's beginning, it was not known whether Pioneer would survive its passage and reach Jupiter. But before sophisticated

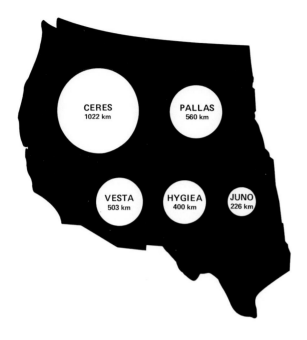

Figure 2-5. Asteroids, or minor planets, are relatively small bodies on the interplanetary scale. Here, five of the largest are shown relative to a map of the Western United States.

Figure 2-6. Asteroids are shown in thousands by photography which reveals them in a time exposure as streaks among the "fixed" stars. The peculiar white streak on the photo is a portrait of an Apollo asteroid taken by Eleanor Helin, Caltech astronomical observer, with the 18-inch Schmidt telescope in July, 1973, at Palomar. It was traveling 97,000 kph (60,000 mph) in relation to the Earth and was photographed at a distance of 13.7 million km (8.5 million miles) from Earth. The exposure time was a little more than two hours. It is calculated that the asteroid is 6-1/2 to 7 km (4 to 4-1/2 miles) in diameter. (*Photo.: Hale Observatories*)

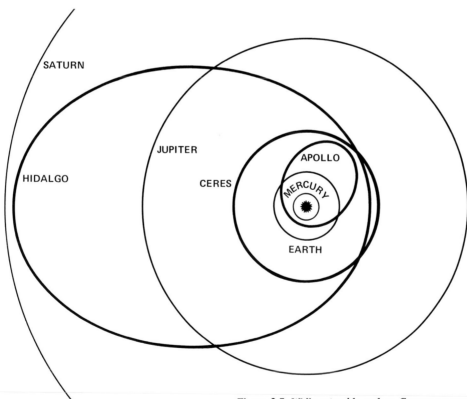

Figure 2-7. While asteroids such as Ceres are generally concentrated in a belt between the orbits of Mars and Jupiter, some stray to the orbit of Mercury (e.g., Apollo) and of Saturn (e.g., Hidalgo). Several have passed relatively close to Earth.

31

missions to the outer planets could be planned, at least one spacecraft had to penetrate and survive passage through the asteroid belt.

A second problem faced by the Pioneer mission to Jupiter was how to supply electrical power to the spacecraft at the great distances it must travel from the Sun. Some of the early mission planning considered using solar cells because radioisotope power generators had not been tested over the long lifetimes required, nor were scientists sure that radiation from such generators would be acceptable to the sensitive scientific equipment carried by the spacecraft. Moreover, the hazard to solar cells by the radiation belts of Jupiter could be even more serious. It was decided not to use them.

Since the spacecraft had to fly very fast to leave Earth, the amount of payload that could be carried was restricted. Complicated on-board computing systems would be too heavy. Jupiter Pioneer had to be virtually "flown from the ground," despite long delay in communications over the distance to Jupiter and beyond.

The long mission period and weight limitations also called for unprecedented high reliability of all the spacecraft components. This was achieved by avoiding complexity in the spacecraft and by keeping the complexity, as much as possible, on the ground. Also vital items, such as transmitters and receivers, were duplicated, and only space-proven systems and components were used. Electronic components were "burned in" before assembly on the spacecraft so that components likely to fail in "infant mortality" were eliminated before the flight.

Success relied very heavily upon an advanced command, control, and communications system to link the Earth-based computers and human controllers to the spacecraft.

Command, Control and Communications

Mission Phases— Four distinct phases of command and control characterized Pioneer's mission to Jupiter and onwards into interstellar space (Figure 2-8). Each called for different approaches

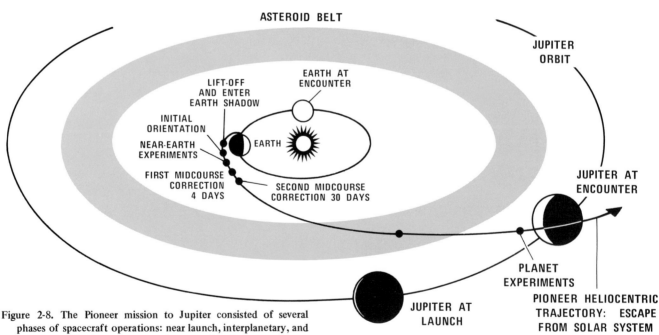

Figure 2-8. The Pioneer mission to Jupiter consisted of several phases of spacecraft operations: near launch, interplanetary, and encounter. The interplanetary phase continued after encounter with Jupiter. If the first Pioneer survived its encounter with Jupiter, the second spacecraft could be directed to a flyby that would hurtle it afterwards towards Saturn for a two-planet mission.

32

and techniques. Two phases — Earth launch and Jupiter encounter — were critical from a standpoint of doing things quickly, of taking necessary corrective actions as soon as possible after events called for them; while the other two phases — interplanetary mode from Earth to Jupiter and beyond Jupiter — permitted more leisurely actions since time was not such a critical factor while the spacecraft traveled between the planetary orbits.

Control of the spacecraft and launch vehicle during the prelaunch and launch phases at NASA's John F. Kennedy Space Center was maintained by launch teams from the Ames and Lewis Research Centers, respectively. Shortly after the spacecraft had been separated from the launch vehicle and had entered into its transfer orbit to Jupiter, spacecraft control was transferred to the Ames flight operations team at the Jet Propulsion Laboratory (JPL) (Figure 2-9). Simultaneously, control of the scientific instruments within the spacecraft was transferred to the Pioneer Mission Operations Center (PMOC) at NASA-Ames Research Center (Figure 2-10). Thus, there was a period of split control between engineering at the Jet Propulsion Laboratory and science at the Pioneer Mission Operations Center. The reason for this split control was to take advantage of the multiple consoles and backup computers at the Jet Propulsion Laboratory for the critical first few days of this epoch-making flight to the outer Solar System.

Engineer specialists were thereby able to monitor, simultaneously, all the systems, such as the spacecraft telemetry, power, thermal, attitude control, data handling, and command subsystems. Operating on three shifts around the clock, they could watch console displays of performance to make sure that each subsystem performed satisfactorily during the period of Pioneer's entry into the environment of space.

Quick reaction to unusual events was mandatory at this time when the spacecraft experienced launch stresses of high acceleration to attain the velocity needed to travel to Jupiter. As Pioneer moved away from the Earth, passing the orbit of the Moon less than 11 hours after liftoff, compared

Figure 2-9. Immediately after liftoff and until the spacecraft settled down and had been thoroughly checked out, use was made of the major facilities of the Space Flight Operations Facility (SFOF) at the Jet Propulsion Laboratory, Pasadena.

Figure 2-10. Control was then passed to the Pioneer Mission Operations Center at NASA-Ames Research Center, Mountain View, California, with continued support from the SFOF.

33

with three days for Apollo to reach the Moon, activities changed from checking the "health" of the spacecraft and its scientific instruments to readying Pioneer for its momentous voyage to and beyond the orbit of Jupiter.

Several days after liftoff, following midcourse maneuvers, and with all equipment and science instruments performing well, the mission crews left the Jet Propulsion Laboratory and the John F. Kennedy Space Center, and returned to NASA Ames Research Center, south of San Francisco in Northern California. Now all control centered here.

Once the spacecraft settled down to the interplanetary mode, spacecraft events were expected to occur more slowly. The task changed to one of watching and waiting and becoming familiar with an increasing delay for signals to go to the spacecraft and return to Earth. In this interplanetary "cruise" phase, all monitoring of the process of "flying" the spacecraft to Jupiter was by a small group at the Pioneer Mission Operations Center, varying between five and seven mission operations people with supporting personnel.

During this interplanetary phase to and beyond Jupiter, engineering and scientific data returning from the spacecraft are continually monitored by computers and by people (Figure 2-11) to provide alerts at the earliest possible moment, should corrective action be required. This action depends upon the circumstances and the urgency of correction. A computer at NASA-Ames Research Center monitors Pioneer's telemetry signals on critical aspects of the spacecraft and its payload. Should a voltage or a temperature or some other engineering parameter rise or fall too much, or the status of an instrument change without being commanded to do so, the computer generates an audible alarm and a printed message. Whatever the hour of day or night, if the situation requires, the duty operator then immediately brings the problem to the attention of the cognizant engineer or scientist who can resolve it. Specific procedures were provided to the trained mission controllers to cover any emergency, should it occur, and to advise them whom to contact for a decision, if the unexpected occurs.

34

Figure 2-11. Duty operators keep constant vigil for the many years of flight watching the spacecraft's performance and that of its scientific instruments.

During the long voyage through interplanetary space, data from each science instrument is sampled periodically to check for scientific "health" as well as engineering "health." Controllers and scientists watch for any need to change bias voltages to adjust range or sensitivity of instruments or to switch modes of operation.

When each Pioneer reached the outskirts of the Jovian system, quick action again became the order of the day. But this was quite different action from the Earth launch phase. Since the Pioneer spacecraft was now over 800 million km (500 million mi.) away, radio signals took 92 minutes for the round trip to the spacecraft and back. All command actions had to be planned well in advance because of this delay.

The most critical item of equipment, in this respect, was the scientific instrument known as the imaging photopolarimeter or IPP for short. This instrument, which is described in detail in Appendix 1, required long sequences of commands during encounter with Jupiter to obtain best possible usage of times when the spacecraft passed by the

Figure 2-12. Communication with the Pioneer spacecraft at unprecedented distances relies upon the large antennas of the Deep Space Net, such as this one at Goldstone in California's Mojave Desert.

planet and by its Galilean satellites. A sequence of contingency commands was designed to reconfigure the Pioneer spacecraft and its instruments, should spurious commands be generated by the build-up of electrical charges or by intense radiation during the close approach to Jupiter.

The fourth and final phase of command and control of Pioneer was entered as each spacecraft passed beyond Jupiter. The mode of operations is similar to that between Earth and Jupiter, but as Pioneer moves farther and farther away from Earth, its signals become increasingly fainter and also take longer and longer to return. Ultimately, contact with the tiny emissaries from Earth will be lost about 1980 for Pioneer 10 and somewhat later for Pioneer 11 if the second spacecraft survives a

planned flyby of Saturn following a successful encounter with Jupiter.

Tracking and Data Acquisition Support— The NASA Communications Network (NASCOM), operated by NASA-Goddard Space Flight Center (GSFC), Maryland, provides worldwide ground communications circuits and facilities that link the Earth terminals of signals received from the spacecraft with the control centers on the West Coast.

Ranged worldwide, the Deep Space Network (DSN) operated for NASA by the Jet Propulsion Laboratory (JPL), provides deep space tracking, telemetry data acquisition, and commanding capabilities through the 26-meter (85-foot) and 64-meter (210-foot) diameter antennas (Figure 2-12) at Goldstone, California, and in Spain, South Africa (until July 1, 1974), and

35

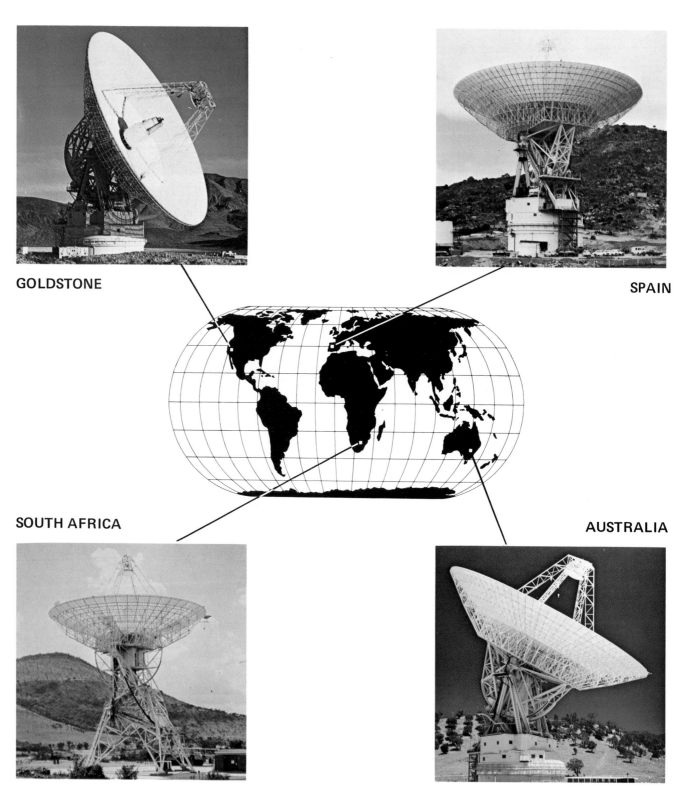

GOLDSTONE

SPAIN

SOUTH AFRICA

AUSTRALIA

Figure 2-13. A world wide network of antennas and communications ensured that as the Earth turned on its axis communication continued with the distant spacecraft on a 24-hour basis through the Deep Space Network.

36

Australia. Thus, as the Earth turns on its axis, the Jupiter Pioneer remains in continuous contact with its controllers; Goldstone, Australia, Spain, or South Africa, operating in turn each day. As Pioneer sets at one station, it is acquired by the next station (Figure 2-13).

Telecommunications– Communications over the vast distances to and beyond Jupiter presented new problems never before faced in the space program. To meet requirements of light weight for the spacecraft, transmitters and antennas aboard had to be designed to conserve power while at the same time being lightweight. Communications with Earth relied a great deal upon the extreme sensitivity of the Deep Space Network's 64-meter (210-foot) antennas and their advanced receiving systems, although the spacecraft can also use the smaller, 26-meter (85-foot) diameter antennas when the 64-meter (210-foot) antennas are required for other space missions.

When used in reverse as transmitters, these 64-meter (210-foot) antennas have such precision of directing a radio beam, and such high radiated power (up to 400,000 watts at Goldstone), that outgoing commands can be received by the spacecraft at greater distances (to several hundred times the distance of Earth from the Sun) than the spacecraft can send its own messages back to Earth (only 20 to 24 times the distance of Earth from the Sun).

The spacecraft carries three antennas – low gain (omni), medium gain, and high gain – used both to receive and to send signals. The spacecraft carries two receivers and two transmitters, which are selected for use by command from Earth.

The amount of energy received over the radio links from the spacecraft at Earth from Jupiter's distance is incredibly small. A 26-meter (85-foot) antenna collecting this energy would require 16.7 million years to gather enough to light a 7-1/2 watt nightlamp for a mere one-thousandth of a second. Only the sophisticated data coding and signal modulation techniques, coupled with the big antennas and the very advanced, ultra-cold, receiving devices attached to them, make it possible to receive and record these faint signals from Pioneer. All the pictures of Jupiter reproduced in this book, all the information from space and the environs of Jupiter, all the engineering data about the spacecraft and its battery of scientific instruments, all the tracking of the spacecraft to nearly a billion miles from the Earth, derive from this incredibly small radio signal. The communications system of Pioneer and the Deep Space Network is truly one of today's great technological achievements.

The rate at which information is passed over a radio link is expressed in bits per second, where a bit is defined as a unit of information, analogous to the dots and dashes of the morse code. Onboard the spacecraft, a data handling system converts science and engineering information into an organized stream of data bits for radio transmission to Earth.

Just as light at night appears fainter and fainter with increasing distance, radio signals from a spacecraft also become fainter with distance. There are also natural, background radio signals, and even the components of electronic apparatus generate radio noise by the movement of electrons within them. So as signals become fainter, they tend to be drowned by the background of noise. Sophisticated techniques have to be employed to receive information over the noise at extreme distances.

As the Pioneer spacecraft move out into the Solar System, their signals, too, become weaker and weaker at Earth. The telemetry system is adapted to the lesser received power by commanding a change in the rate at which information is transmitted to Earth. Power per unit of information depends upon the rate at which the information is sent; the bit rate. To extract information from a radio signal, there must be a certain energy in the signal in excess of the energy of the background noise. As the range to the spacecraft increases, the bit rate is reduced so that less information is sent per second. But each bit of information lasts longer and possesses more energy so that it can be detected above the radio noise.

By reducing the bit rate, controllers compensated for the reduced received signal strength from Pioneer. On the way to Jupiter, the Pioneer communications system could pass a maximum of 2,048 bits of information to Earth every second, using the 26-meter (85-foot) antennas. But at Jupiter, the maximum rate could only be 1,024 bits per second, using the 64-meter (210-foot) antennas, because of the increased range.

A digital telemetry unit on the spacecraft prepares the data for transmission in one of 13 data formats at one of 8 bit rates of from 16 to 2,048 bits per second. An onboard data storage unit is able to store 49,152 data bits for later transmission to Earth. This permits data to be gathered by Pioneer during important parts of the mission faster than the spacecraft can send the data to Earth or when no data could be transmitted at all, for example, when the spacecraft was being occulted by Jupiter. The data is then later transmitted in response to ground command.

Command and Control– Controllers at Pioneer Mission Operations Control use 222 different commands to operate the Pioneer spacecraft. The command system consists of two command decoders and a command distribution unit within the spacecraft. Commands are transmitted from Earth at a rate of one bit per second. Since each command message consists of 22 bits, a command requires 22 seconds for its transmission.

The spacecraft also carries a small command memory to provide storage onboard of five commands. When a series of up to five commands must be executed in less time than that needed to transmit them from Earth, i.e., 22 seconds for each, this storage is used. The command memory with time delay was also used to command the spacecraft when behind Jupiter and out of touch with Earth.

A command distribution unit routes the commands to destinations within the spacecraft: 73 to operate experiments and 149 to control spacecraft subsystems. Science commands, for example, include those to calibrate instruments, change modes, move the photopolarimeter telescope, and change instrument data types. Spacecraft commands include firing the rocket thrusters and changing from one component to another redundant component, selecting different antennas, and changing the modes of the data handling subsystem.

Any command not properly verified by the decoder in the spacecraft is not acted upon by the command distribution unit. Thus, precautions are taken against the spacecraft accepting wrong commands. Commands are also verified on the ground by the computer and by controllers before transmission. A Pioneer Encounter Planning Team looked at many possible contingencies that might arise during the weeks that each Pioneer would spend passing through the Jovian system, and developed command sequences to meet them.

The decision, made early during planning, that the spacecraft would be "flown" by command, demanded constant thinking, planning, and acting well in advance of events occurring on the spacecraft. Indeed, two years of planning preceded the first encounter with Jupiter. All commands (over 16,000 in all for Pioneer 10) were meticulously sequenced and each was timed to be executed within one tenth of a second of a scheduled time. These were checked and stored in a computer in eight-hour long files suitable for transmission during the time that a ground station would be in contact with the distant spacecraft. The majority of these commands was transmitted to the spacecraft in a four-week period. This was an outstanding achievement and performance on the part of all personnel concerned at the Pioneer Mission Operations Center, the Ground Data System, and the Deep Space Network in sending the commands on time and with the high reliability needed for the Jupiter encounter.

3
The Pioneer Jupiter Spacecraft

THE JUPITER PIONEER spacecraft were designed to fit within the 3-meter (10-foot) diameter shroud of the Atlas-Centaur launch vehicle. To do so each spacecraft had to be stowed with its booms retracted, and with its antenna dish facing forward, i.e., upward on the launch pad. Its basic characteristics are extreme reliability, very light weight, a communications system for extreme distances, and a nonsolar heat source for electrical power generation.

Figure 3-1 is a diagram of the Pioneer spacecraft. Each spacecraft comprises several distinct subsystems: a general structure, an attitude control and propulsion system, a communications system, thermal control system, electrical power system, navigation system, and, most important to the scientific mission, a payload of 11 sophisticated onboard instruments.

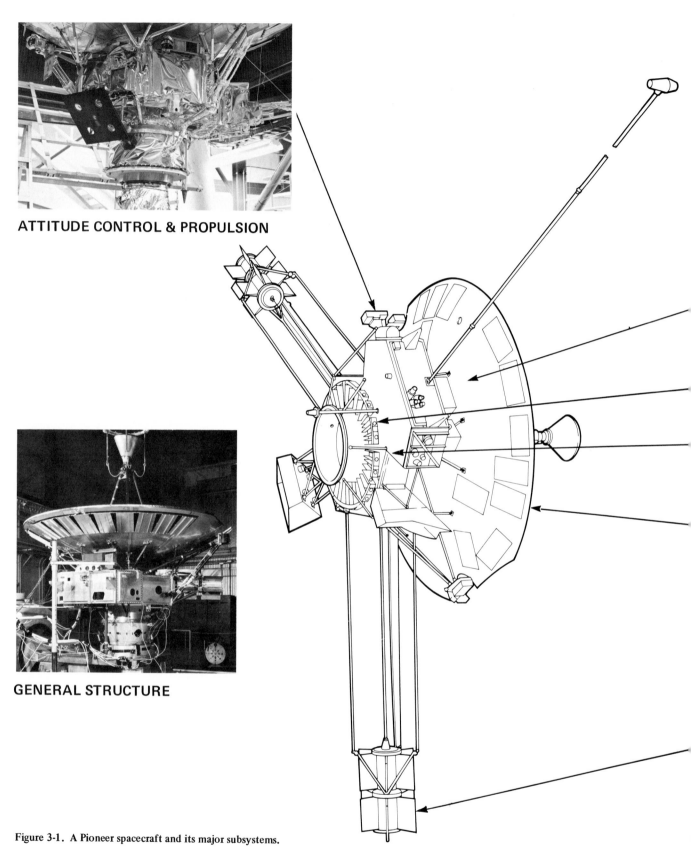

ATTITUDE CONTROL & PROPULSION

GENERAL STRUCTURE

Figure 3-1. A Pioneer spacecraft and its major subsystems.

40

NAVIGATION

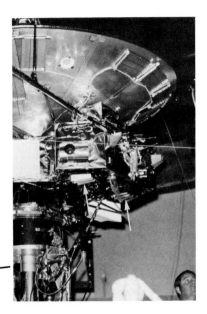

THERMAL CONTROL

SCIENCE EXPERIMENTS

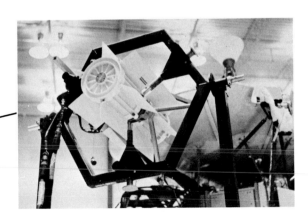

ELECTRICAL POWER

COMMUNICATIONS

To communicate over long distances the spacecraft's dish-shaped antenna has to be pointed toward Earth. A simple and inexpensive way to do this is to spin stabilize the spacecraft and keep the spin axis pointed to Earth. So the spacecraft is stabilized by rotation (Figure 3-2).

General Structure

Each spacecraft is 2.9-meters (9-1/2 feet) long from its cone-shaped, medium-gain antenna to the adapter ring which fastened the spacecraft to stage three of the launch vehicle.

Spacecraft structure centers around a 36-cm (14-inch) deep, flat, equipment compartment, the top and bottom of which are regular hexagons. Its sides are each 71-cm (28-inches) long. One joins to a smaller "squashed" hexagonal compartment that carries most of the scientific experiments.

The 2.74-meter (9-foot) diameter, 46-cm (18-inch) deep, parabolic, dish-shaped, high-gain antenna of aluminum honeycomb sandwich material is attached to the front of the equipment compartment. Its feed is topped with a medium-gain antenna on three struts which project about 1.2 meters (4 feet) forward. A low-gain, omni antenna extends about 0.76 meters (2-1/2 feet) behind the equipment compartment, mounted below the high-gain dish.

Two three-rod trusses, 120 degrees apart, project from two sides of the equipment compartment. At their ends, nuclear electric power generators are held about 3 meters (10 feet) from the center of the spacecraft. A third boom, 120 degrees from the other two, projects from the experiment compartment and positions a magnetometer sensor about 6.6 meters (21-1/2 feet) from the center of the spacecraft. All three booms are extended after launch.

Attitude Control and Propulsion

The spacecraft possesses a star sensor to provide a reference on the bright southern star Canopus, and two sun sensors to provide a reference to the

42

Figure 3-2. Each Pioneer spacecraft is stabilized by rotation as shown under test here.

Sun. Attitude position is calculated from the reference direction to the Earth and the Sun, with the known direction to Canopus provided as backup. Pioneer 11's star sensor gain and threshold settings were modified to improve performance based on experience with this sensor on Pioneer 10.

Three pairs of rocket thrusters located near the rim of the antenna dish (Figure 3-3) are used to direct the spin axis of the spacecraft, to keep it spinning at the desired rate of 4.8 revolutions per minute, and to change the spacecraft's velocity. The system's six thruster nozzles can be fired steadily or pulsed by command.

Each thruster develops its propulsive jet force from the decomposition of liquid hydrazine by a catalyst in a small rocket thrust chamber attached to the nozzle of the thrusters.

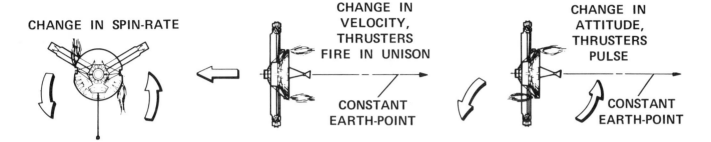

CHANGE IN SPIN-RATE

CHANGE IN VELOCITY, THRUSTERS FIRE IN UNISON

CONSTANT EARTH-POINT

CHANGE IN ATTITUDE, THRUSTERS PULSE

CONSTANT EARTH-POINT

Figure 3-3. Thrusters are used to control the spin of the spacecraft, its attitude, and its velocity.

Attitude and velocity changes are made by two thruster pairs mounted on opposite sides of the antenna dish rim. One thruster of each pair points forward, the other, aft. To change attitude, the spacecraft spin axis is rotated in the desired direction by firing two thrusters, one on each side of the antenna dish. One thruster is fired forward, one aft, in brief thrust pulses at a precise position in the circle of spacecraft rotation. Each thrust pulse, timed to the spacecraft's rotation, moves (precesses) the spin axis a few tenths of a degree, until the desired attitude is reached.

To change velocity, the spin axis is precessed until it points in the desired direction, then two thruster nozzles, one on each side of the antenna dish, are fired continuously, both in the same direction, i.e., forward or aft to increase or decrease the flight path velocity.

To adjust spin rate, two more pairs of thrusters, also set along the rim of the antenna dish, are used. These thrusters are aligned tangentially to the antenna rim, one pointing against the direction of spin and the other with it. Thus to reduce spin rate, two thrusters fire against spin direction.

Communications

The spacecraft carries two identical receivers. The omni and medium-gain antennas operate together and as such are connected to one receiver while the high-gain is connected to the other, though the receivers do not operate together. The receivers can be interchanged by command, or, should there be a period of inactivity, automatically. Thus, should a receiver fail during the mission, the other can automatically take over.

Two radio transmitters, coupled to two traveling-wave-tube power amplifiers, each produce 8 watts of power in S-band.

The communication frequency uplink from Earth to the spacecraft is at 2110 MHz, the downlink to Earth at 2292 MHz. The turnaround ratio, downlink to uplink, is precisely controlled to be compatible with the Deep Space Network.

The spacecraft data system turns science and engineering information into a specially coded stream of data bits for radio transmission to Earth. A convolutional encoder rearranges the data in a form that allows detection and correction of most errors by a ground computer at the receiving site of the Deep Space Network. There are 11 data formats divided into science and engineering data groups. Some science formats are optimized for interplanetary data, others for the Jovian encounter. Engineering data formats specialize in data handling, electrical, communications, orientation, and propulsion data. All formats are selected by ground command.

Thermal Control

Temperature on the spacecraft is controlled at between −23° C and 38° C (−10° and 100° F) inside the scientific instrument compartment, and at various other levels elsewhere for satisfactory operation of the onboard equipment.

The temperature control system coped with gradually decreasing heating as the spacecraft moved away from the Sun, and with two frigid periods — one when Pioneer 10 passed through Earth's shadow at launch; the other at the time of passage through Jupiter's shadow during flyby. The system also controlled the effects of heat from the third-stage engine, atmosphere friction, spacecraft nuclear electric power generators, and other equipment.

The equipment compartments are insulated by multi-layered blankets of aluminized plastic. Temperature-responsive louvers at the bottom of the equipment compartment, opened by bi-metallic springs, allow controlled escape of excess heat. Other equipment has individual thermal insulation and is warmed by electric heaters and 12 one-watt radioisotope heaters, fueled with plutonium-238.

Electrical Power

Nuclear-fueled electric power for Pioneer Jupiter comes from the four SNAP-19 type Radioisotope Thermoelectric Generators (RTGs), developed by the Atomic Energy Commission (AEC), similar to those used to power the Nimbus-3 meteorological satellite. These units turn heat from plutonium-238 into electricity (Figure 3-4).

The RTGs (Figure 3-5) are on the opposite side of the spacecraft from the scientific instrument compartment to reduce the effects of their neutron radiation on the instruments. Mounted two each on the end of each boom, these four RTGs developed about 155 watts of electrical power at launch, which decayed to approximately 140 watts by the time the spacecraft reached Jupiter. One hundred watts output is expected five years after launch. The depletion of power is not from the nuclear source itself but from deterioration of the junctions of the thermocouples which convert heat into electricity. The RTGs supply adequate power for the mission since the spacecraft needs only 100 watts to operate all systems, of which 26 watts are for the science instruments. Excess power from

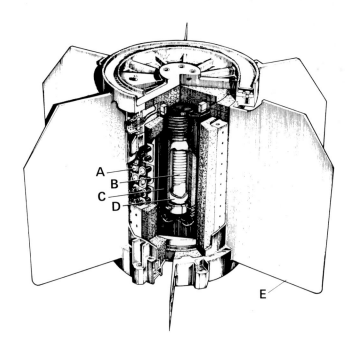

A   THERMOELECTRICS
B   FUEL CAPSULE
C   REENTRY HEAT SHIELD
D   FUEL DISCS
E   HEAT RADIATING FINS

Figure 3-4. Electrical power is developed in Pioneer by several radioisotope thermoelectric generators (RTG).

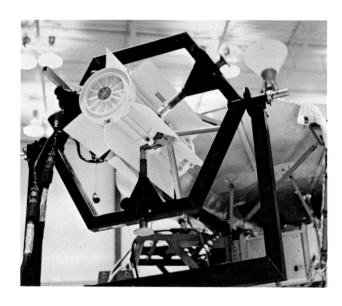

Figure 3-5. Two RTGs are mounted at the end of each of two extended booms to reduce nuclear radiation effects on the sensitive scientific instruments.

44

the RTGs over that needed by the spacecraft is radiated to space thermally through a shunt radiator, or charges a battery which automatically supplies additional power needed for short periods when the spacecraft demands more power than the output of the RTGs.

Navigation

The axis of the high-gain antenna dish is slightly offset from, but parallel to, the spin axis of the spacecraft within close tolerances throughout the mission. Except during initial stages of the flight near Earth and for periods when alignment must be changed to suit course correction, the spin axis of the spacecraft is always pointed toward Earth within a tolerance of one degree to provide best communication.

Analysts use the shift in frequency of the Pioneer radio signal and angle tracking by the antennas of the Deep Space Net to calculate the speed, distance, and direction of the spacecraft from Earth. Motion of the spacecraft away from Earth causes the frequency of the spacecraft's radio signals to drop and their wavelength to increase. Known as a Doppler shift, this effect allows the speed of the spacecraft to be calculated from measurement of the frequency change in the signal received at Earth.

The radio beam is offset one degree from the spin axis. As a result, when the spin axis is not directed exactly towards Earth, uplink signals received at the spacecraft from Earth vary in intensity synchronously with rotation of the spacecraft. A system on the spacecraft, known as Conical Scan (CONSCAN) (Figure 3-6), was originally intended to be automatically used to change the spacecraft's attitude in a direction to reduce these variations in signal strength, thereby returning the spin axis to the precise Earth point to within the threshold of 0.3 degrees. However, flight operations personnel developed and used a direct command technique that results in conserving the spacecraft's gas supply.

Scientific Payload

Investigation of interplanetary space on the way to and beyond Jupiter aimed to resolve a number of unknowns about the magnetic field in interplanetary space; cosmic rays, fast moving parts of atoms from both the Sun and the Galaxy; the solar wind, a flow of charged particles from the Sun, and its relationships with the interplanetary magnetic field and cosmic rays; and interplanetary dust concentrations, if any, in the asteroid belt.

At Jupiter the spacecraft investigated the Jovian system in three main ways: measurement of particles, fields and radiation, spin-scan imaging to provide pictures of the planet and some of its satellites, and additionally, by accurate observation of the path of the spacecraft, measurement of the forces — the gravity of Jupiter and the Galilean satellites — acting upon it.

To achieve these scientific objectives, each Pioneer spacecraft carries the scientific experiments described in the next chapter.

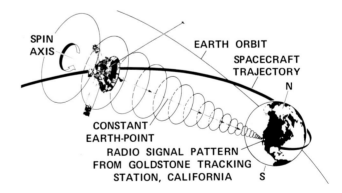

Figure 3-6. An automatic system in the spacecraft, known as CONSCAN, is used to help keep the spin axis of Pioneer pointing toward Earth. It relies upon a slight offset in the antenna feed axis to produce a wobbling signal at Earth when the antenna is not pointing exactly Earthwards. Controllers direct the spacecraft so that its antenna drifts past the optimum point and thereby they conserve thruster propellant. With more expenditure of propellant, CONSCAN could point the spacecraft's axis automatically.

4
Pioneer Science at New Frontiers

THE SCIENTIFIC PAYLOADS of both Pioneer 10 and Pioneer 11 are designed to gather new knowledge on interplanetary space beyond Mars and on the Jovian system. Basically, several science instruments measure particles, fields, and radiation, while an imaging photopolarimeter provides spin-scan imaging and analysis of scattered light. Additionally, the spacecraft's radio signal is used to measure the Jovian gravitational fields, and to investigate the atmospheres of Jupiter and its satellites.

The Pioneers perform several experiments between Earth and Jupiter and beyond Jupiter:

★ Maps the magnetic field in interplanetary space.

★ Determines how the solar wind changes with distance from the Sun.

★ Measures cosmic rays originating both from within and from outside the Solar System.

★ Studies interactions among the interplanetary magnetic field, the solar wind and cosmic rays.

★ Searches for the transition region of the heliosphere — the region where the influence of the Sun on interplanetary space terminates.

★ Measures the amount of neutral hydrogen — un-ionized hydrogen atoms — in interplanetary space and at Jupiter.

★ Ascertains the distribution of dust particles in interplanetary space.

★ Determines the size, mass, flux, and velocity of small particles in the asteroid belt and thus provides information on the possible hazard to a spacecraft passing through this belt.

Within the Jovian system, each Pioneer performs another series of experiments:

★ Maps the Jovian magnetic field: its intensity, direction, and structure.

★ Determines how many electrons and protons of various energies are distributed along the trajectory of the spacecraft through the Jovian magnetosphere.

★ Searches for auroras in the polar atmosphere of Jupiter.

★ Obtains information to help interpret the observed characteristics of the two main types of radio waves from Jupiter, decimetric and decametric.

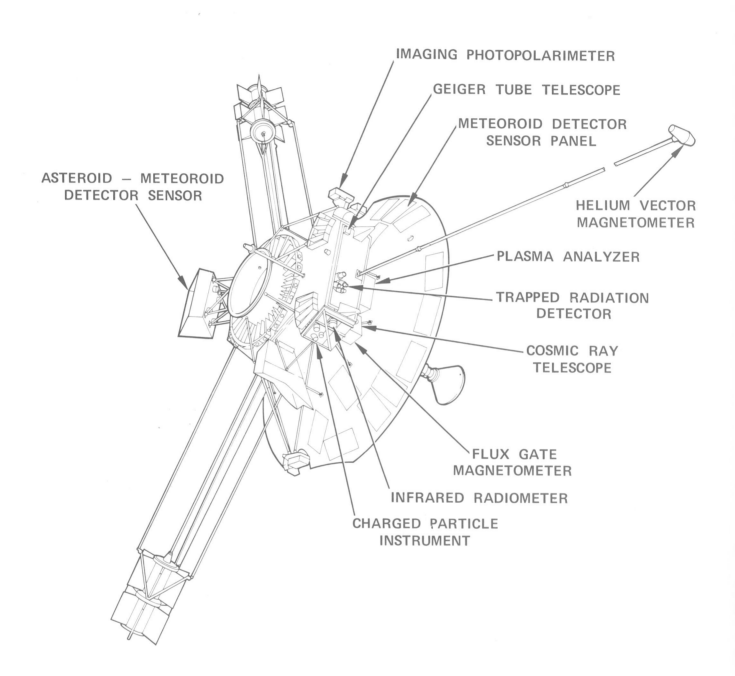

IMAGING PHOTOPOLARIMETER

GEIGER TUBE TELESCOPE

METEOROID DETECTOR
SENSOR PANEL

ASTEROID — METEOROID
DETECTOR SENSOR

HELIUM VECTOR
MAGNETOMETER

PLASMA ANALYZER

TRAPPED RADIATION
DETECTOR

COSMIC RAY
TELESCOPE

FLUX GATE
MAGNETOMETER

INFRARED RADIOMETER

CHARGED PARTICLE
INSTRUMENT

Figure 4-1. Each Pioneer carries eleven science experiments.

★ Maps the interaction of the Jovian system with the solar wind.

★ Measures the temperature of Jupiter's atmosphere and of some of the large Jovian satellites.

★ Determines the structure of the upper atmosphere of Jupiter where molecules become electrically charged to form an ionosphere.

★ Maps Jovian thermal structure by measurement of infrared radiation.

★ Obtains spin-scan images of Jupiter in two colors during the encounter sequence and close up images of special planetary features, and makes polarimetry measurements of Jupiter and some of its large satellites.

★ Probes the Jovian atmosphere with S-band radio waves at occultation: similarly probes the Galilean satellite Io to investigate its atmospheric characteristics.

★ Investigates as many as possible of the Galilean satellites at close range by spin-scan imaging and other measurements to aid in determining their size and physical characteristics.

★ Determines more precisely the masses of Jupiter and its four large satellites by accurate observation of the effects of their gravitational fields on the motion of the spacecraft.

★ Provides information to calculate with greater accuracy the orbits and ephemerides of Jupiter and the Galilean satellites.

Eleven scientific instruments (Figure 4-1) were selected from over 150 proposals submitted to NASA Headquarters in response to the announcement of the Pioneer Jupiter flight opportunity. These instruments, and two non-instrumented experiments, are described below.

Magnetic Fields

Magnetic fields affect the plasma of electrically charged particles in interplanetary space and control the flow of this plasma as it spreads out from the Sun across the orbits of the planets. Before the mission of Pioneer 10 these effects had been only observed and measured out to the orbit of Mars. Scientists were still uncertain about many specific details about the interplanetary medium and particularly the extent to which the Sun's magnetic field controlled the flow of plasma beyond Mars to the outer regions of the Solar System. The outer boundaries of this influence were, and still are, vague, and interactions between the plasma and fields of the Solar System and those of the Galactic System still puzzle scientists. Pioneer 10 and Pioneer 11 will continue to explore the regions beyond the orbit of Jupiter and will make measurements that will help define the transition region of solar influence (heliosphere).

The principal investigator for this experiment is Edward J. Smith, Jet Propulsion Laboratory, Pasadena, California. Coinvestigators are: Palmer Dyal and David S. Colburn, NASA-Ames Research Center, Mountain View, California; Charles P. Sonett, University of Arizona; Douglas E. Jones, Brigham Young University, Provo, Utah; Paul J. Coleman, Jr., University of California at Los Angeles; and Leverett Davis, Jr., California Institute of Technology, Pasadena.

This experiment uses a sensitive magnetometer (Figure 4-2) at the tip of a lightweight boom, which extends 6.6 meters (21-1/2 feet) from the center of the spacecraft to reduce the effects of even the minute residual spacecraft magnetic field, and to assist the balance of this spin stabilized spacecraft. The helium vector magnetometer measures the fine structure of the interplanetary field, maps the Jovian field, and provides field measurements to evaluate solar wind interaction with Jupiter. The magnetometer operates in any one of eight different ranges, the lowest of which covers magnetic fields from ±0.01 to ±4.0 gamma; the highest, fields up to ±140,000 gamma; i.e., ±1.4 Gauss.

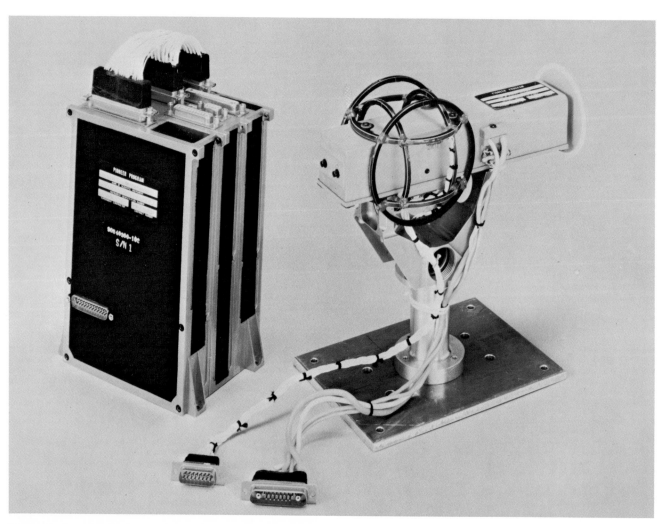

Figure 4-2. The magnetometer, mounted on a long boom to keep it far away from the RTGs measures magnetic fields in space and in the vicinity of Jupiter. The electronics at the left of the magnetometer are mounted in the spacecraft.

(The surface field of the Earth is approximately 0.5 Gauss.) The ranges are selected by ground command or automatically by the instrument itself as it reaches the limits of a given range.

The sensor for the magnetometer consists of a cell filled with helium that is excited by electrical discharge at radio frequencies and infrared optical pumping. Changes in helium absorption caused by magnetic fields passing through the magnetometer are measured by an infrared optical detector.

Interplanetary Solar Wind and the Heliosphere

The principal investigator for this experiment is John H. Wolfe of NASA-Ames Research Center, with coinvestigators John Mihalov, H. Collard, and D. D. McKibbin of NASA-Ames Research Center; Louis A. Frank, University of Iowa, Iowa City; Reimar Lust, Max Planck Institut fur Physik und Astrophysik, Garching, Germany; Devrie Intriligator, University of Southern California; and William C. Feldman, Los Alamos Scientific Laboratory, New Mexico.

50

The solar wind of highly ionized, electrically charged particles continually sweeping out into interplanetary space from the Sun affects electrical and communications systems on Earth and may give rise to long-term weather cycles. This wind was unknown until spacecraft began to explore space beyond the Earth's magnetosphere less than 15 years ago. Some of the charged particles of the solar wind become trapped in radiation belts by the Earth's magnetic field. They also account for the aurora borealis and aurora australis and other phenomena which baffled scientists until the radiation belts were discovered by experiments carried on Earth satellites.

How the solar wind behaves at great distances from the Sun was highly conjectural before the flight of Pioneer 10. Instruments on spacecraft had only measured the wind as far as the orbit of Mars.

The instrument carried by each spacecraft to evaluate the solar wind to the orbit of Jupiter and beyond is a plasma analyzer that looks toward the Sun through a hole in the spacecraft's large dish-shaped antenna (Figure 4-3). The solar wind enters the plasma analyzer apertures between 2 quadraspherical plates where the direction of arrival, the energy (speed), and the number of ions and electrons making up the solar wind are measured.

The instrument has a high resolution and a medium resolution analyzer to detect particles of different energy levels. Energies of these particles are described in terms of units called electron volts (eV).

A voltage is applied across the quadraspherical plates in a maximum of 64 steps, at a rate of one step per spacecraft revolution, to count particles in discrete energy ranges. Direction of particle travel is found from the way the instrument is pointed and from the particular target within the instrument that detects it.

The high resolution analyzer has 26 continuous-channel multipliers (CCM) to measure the number of ions per second between 100 and 8,000 electron volts. The medium resolution analyzer has five electrometers to count ions of 100 to 18,000 electron volts and electrons of 1 to 500 electron volts.

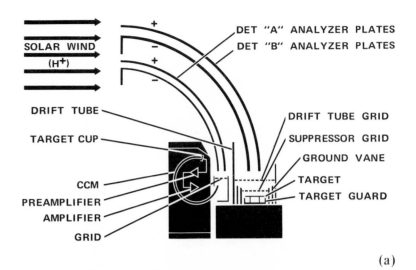

(a)

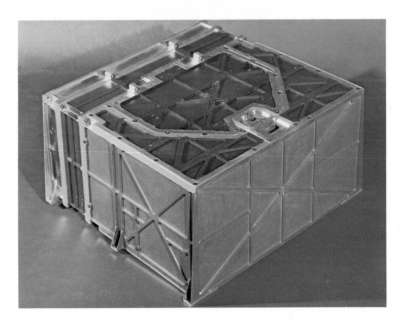

(b)

Figure 4-3. A plasma analyzer peers through a hole in the large dish-shaped antenna to detect particles of the solar wind originating from the Sun. (a) Shows the instrument in diagrammatic form. (b) Shows it ready for installation in the spacecraft.

Charged Particle Composition

Principal investigator for this experiment is John A. Simpson, University of Chicago. Coinvestigators are Joseph J. O'Gallagher, University of Maryland, College Park, and Anthony J. Tuzzolino, University of Chicago.

Figure 4-4. Charged particle detectors are used to study the life history of cosmic rays in the Solar System.

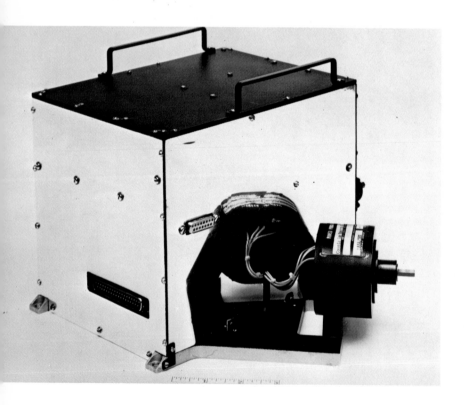

Figure 4-5. A combination of cosmic ray telescopes seeks further information on the composition of the cosmic ray particles and their energy ranges.

The charged particle detector (Figure 4-4) has four measuring systems: two particle telescopes that operate in interplanetary space, and two that measure the intense trapped electrons and protons inside the Jovian radiation belts.

During the interplanetary phase of the mission, before and after encounter with Jupiter, the experiment sought to identify the chemical elements hydrogen, helium, lithium, beryllium, boron, carbon, and nitrogen, and to separate hydrogen, deuterium, helium-3 and helium-4 in an attempt to differentiate between particles coming from the Sun and those from the Galaxy. The instrument is also used to determine how the streams of high energy particles from the Sun travel through interplanetary space. The main telescope of seven solid-state detectors measures the composition of cosmic rays from 1 to 500 million electron volts (MeV), and a three-element, low energy telescope measures 0.4 to 10 MeV protons and helium nuclei.

Two new types of sensors were developed to cope with the extremely high intensities of trapped radiation in the magnetosphere of Jupiter. A solid-state electron current detector, operating below $-40°$ C $(-104°$ F), detects those electrons above 3 MeV that generate the decimetric radio waves emitted from Jupiter. A trapped proton detector contains a foil of thorium which undergoes nuclear fission when impacted with protons above 30 MeV, but is insensitive to electrons.

Energy Spectra of Cosmic Rays

Frank B. McDonald, NASA-Goddard Space Flight Center, Greenbelt, Maryland, is principal investigator for this experiment, with coinvestigators Kenneth G. McCracken, Minerals Research Laboratory, North Ryde, Australia; William R. Webber and Edmond C. Roelof, University of New Hampshire, Durham; and Bonnard J. Teegarden and James H. Trainor, NASA-Goddard Space Flight Center.

The cosmic ray telescope used for this experiment (Figure 4-5) is also designed to monitor solar and galactic cosmic rays and track the twisting high energy particles from the Sun. The instrument can determine which of the nuclei of the ten lightest elements make up these cosmic ray particles. Before saturation by radiation, the cosmic ray telescope measured high energy particles in Jupiter's radiation belts.

The instrument consists of three, three-element, solid-state telescopes. The high energy telescope measures the flux of protons between 56 and 800 MeV. The medium energy telescope measures protons with energies between 3 and 22 MeV, and identifies the ten elements from hydrogen to neon. The low energy telescope measures the flux of electrons between .05 and 1 MeV, and of protons between .05 and 20 MeV.

Charged Particles in the Jovian System

Principal investigator for this experiment is James A. Van Allen, University of Iowa, Iowa City. A Geiger tube telescope characterizes Jupiter's radiation belts using seven Geiger-Müller tubes to survey the intensities, energy spectra, and angular distributions of electrons and protons along the spacecraft's path through the radiation belts of Jupiter. The instrument is shown in Figure 4-6.

Each tube is a small gas filled cylinder. When a charged particle passes through the gas, an electrical signal is generated. Three parallel tubes form a telescope. Three others form a triangular array to measure the number of multi-particle events called showers. The combination of telescope and shower detector compares primary and secondary events in the Jovian radiation belts. The third telescope detects low energy electrons above 40 keV. The instrument also counts protons with energies above 5 MeV and electrons with energies from 2 to 50 MeV.

Trapped Radiation in the Jovian System

Using different types of telescopes from the previous experiment, a trapped radiation detector is designed to cover a broader range of energies of

Figure 4-6. Other telescopes are used to explore the radiation belts of Jupiter, measuring electrons and protons in these belts.

electrons and protons. Principal investigator is R. Walker Fillius, University of California at San Diego, with Carl E. McIlwain of the same University as coinvestigator.

The greater range of this instrument is obtained through use of several different kinds of detectors. An unfocused Cerenkov counter detects the light emitted in a particular direction as particles pass through it. It records electrons of energy 0.5 to 12 MeV. An electron scatter detector is activated by electrons at 100 to 400 keV.

The instrument also includes a minimum ionizing detector consisting of a solid-state diode that

53

Figure 4-7. The radiation is further explored over an even broader range of energies by a trapped radiation detector.

measures minimum ionizing particles (i.e., less than 3 MeV) and protons in the range of 50 to 350 MeV.

Different sensitive materials in two scintillation detectors distinguish roughly between electrons of less than 5 and protons of less than 50 keV.

These five different "eyes" of the instrument (Figure 4-7) provide basic information about several of the fundamental features of Jupiter's radiation belts including the types of particles within the belts, their distribution, energy, and intensity.

Particles and Dust in Space

This investigation consists of two distinct experiments using different experimental techniques; one to detect light reflected from particles, the other to detect impact of particles.

Principal investigator for the first experiment is Robert K. Soberman, General Electric Company, Philadelphia, whose coinvestigator is Herbert A. Zook, NASA-Manned Spacecraft Center, Houston, Texas. The instrument (Figure 4-8) consists of four non-imaging telescopes that detect sunlight reflected from meteoroids passing through their fields of view. Each telescope has a 20 cm (8-inch) diameter primary mirror, secondary optics, and a photomultiplier tube that converts light to electrical signals. When a particle passes through the telescope's 8-degree field of view, reflected light is detected by the photomultiplier tube. The four telescope's fields of view overlap slightly. If a particle is "seen" simultaneously by any three of the telescopes an event is recorded. From this data the particle's distance, trajectory, velocity, and relative size may be calculated.

These telescopes are capable of detecting objects ranging from distant asteroids miles in diameter to minute sunlit particles of dust several feet from the telescopes.

The second experiment has William H. Kinard, NASA-Langley Research Center, Hampton, Virginia, as principal investigator. Coinvestigators are José M. Alvarez, Robert L. O'Neal, Donald H. Humes and Richard E. Turner, also of NASA-Langley Research Center.

(b)

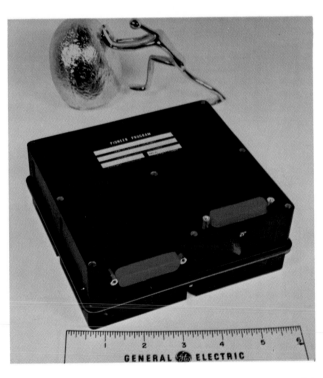

(a)

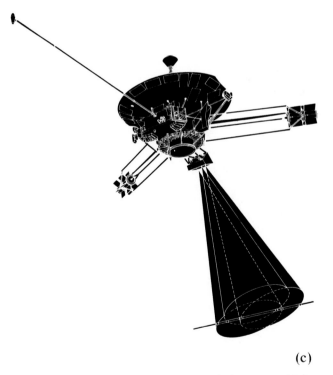

(c)

Figure 4-8. A meteoroid-asteroid detector looks into space with four non-imaging telescopes to track particles ranging from close-by bits of dust to distant large asteroids. Shows (a) the electronics, (b) the four non-imaging telescopes, and (c) how this experiment is mounted on the spacecraft.

55

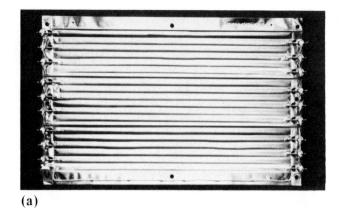

(a)

(b)

(c)

Figure 4-9. Twelve panels of pressurized cells mounted on the back of the main dish antenna record penetrating impacts of small meteoroids. Shows (a) one panel, (b) its electronics, and (c) how the panels were mounted behind the antenna.

The meteoroid detector consists of 13 panels, each containing 18 sealed cells pressurized with argon and nitrogen. These panels cover 0.605 square meters (6.5 square feet) of the back of the main antenna dish (Figure 4-9).

When a cell is punctured by particulate matter in interplanetary space it loses gas at a rate proportional to the size of the hole made in the tube.

The experiment indicates penetration by meteoroids having masses of one billionth of a gram and larger. Panels on Pioneer 11 are made up of cells with thicker wall material to detect particles of greater mass.

Ultraviolet Photometry

This ultraviolet photometer (Figure 4-10) investigates the ultraviolet reflective properties or emission from interplanetary hydrogen, helium and dust, and from Jupiter's atmosphere and satellites. Its principal investigator is Darrell L. Judge, University of Southern California, Los Angeles, with Robert W. Carlson of the same university as coinvestigator.

Radiotelescopes have shown that the Solar System is immersed in and traveling through an interstellar gas of cold, neutral (uncharged) hydrogen. By measuring the scattering of the Sun's ultraviolet light in space the Pioneer instrument seeks to measure the amount of this neutral hydrogen within the heliosphere. Presence of such neutral hydrogen (already measured near Earth) could be the result of neutralization of fast solar wind hydrogen ions at the heliosphere boundary, their conversion into fast uncharged hydrogen atoms, and their diffusion back into the heliosphere. Or they may be coming in from the Galaxy itself; penetrating the Solar System as a result of the system's 73,000 km/hr (45,000 miles per hour) velocity through the interstellar gas.

The experiment may ultimately provide data to resolve the origin of the neutral hydrogen and establish the boundaries of the heliosphere. From measurements of the interplanetary helium, experimenters hope to determine the percentage of this gas in the interstellar medium. This may perhaps

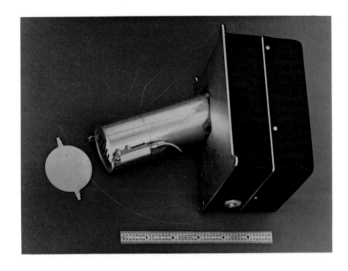

(a)

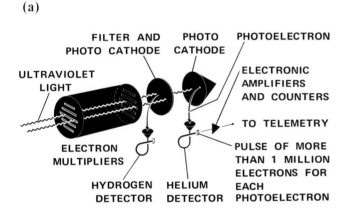

FILTER AND PHOTO CATHODE

PHOTO CATHODE

PHOTOELECTRON

ULTRAVIOLET LIGHT

ELECTRONIC AMPLIFIERS AND COUNTERS

TO TELEMETRY

ELECTRON MULTIPLIERS

PULSE OF MORE THAN 1 MILLION ELECTRONS FOR EACH PHOTOELECTRON

HYDROGEN DETECTOR

HELIUM DETECTOR

(b)

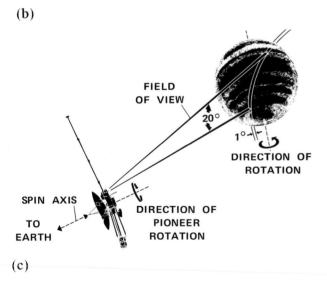

FIELD OF VIEW

20°

1°

DIRECTION OF ROTATION

SPIN AXIS

TO EARTH

DIRECTION OF PIONEER ROTATION

(c)

Figure 4-10. Ultraviolet light is sensed by this ultraviolet photometer to determine the quantities of hydrogen and helium in space and on Jupiter. (a) Is a photograph and (b) a diagram of the instrument. (c) Shows how it scans Jupiter.

confirm or deny the "big bang" theory — a single creative event rather than continuous creation — for the origin of the universe which postulates seven percent helium in the interstellar gas.

The ultraviolet photometer has a fixed viewing angle and uses the spin of the spacecraft to scan around the celestial sphere. When close to Jupiter, the photometer scans the medium above the cloud tops. By measuring the changes in the intensity of ultraviolet light reflected into two photocathodes of the instrument — one measuring radiation at 1216 Angstroms, the other at 584 Angstroms — the photometer detects light from hydrogen and helium respectively.

Within the Jovian system the photometer measures the scattering of solar ultraviolet light by the atmosphere of Jupiter. This scattering provides information on the amount of atomic hydrogen in Jupiter's upper atmosphere, the mixing rate of Jupiter's atmosphere, the amount of helium there, and therefore the ratio of helium to hydrogen at Jupiter. Virtually all theories of Jupiter's origin and development make assumptions about the amount of helium in the planet's atmosphere, but prior to Pioneer 10's mission helium had not been identified at the planet.

By measuring changes in the ultraviolet light glow the instrument checks to see if Jupiter has polar auroras, bright glowing parts of the upper atmosphere caused by concentration of particles along magnetic field lines from space towards the poles of the planet.

Infrared Radiometry

Infrared emissions from Jupiter have been measured successfully from Earth. Maps of the planet at this wavelength have been made and show belts and bands similar to visible light pictures. But most of the planet's infrared radiation is emitted at 20 to 40 micrometers and these wavelengths can be observed effectively only by a spacecraft since the Earth's atmosphere readily absorbs them, blocking the 40 micrometers region entirely. The infrared radiometer is designed to measure radiation from Jupiter at 20 and 40 micrometer wavelengths.

57

Principal investigator is Guido Münch, California Institute of Technology; his coinvestigators are Gerry Neugebauer, also of Caltech; Stillman C. Chase, Santa Barbara Research Center; and Laurence M. Trafton, University of Texas, Austin.

Perhaps the most important question about Jupiter is its heat balance — the balance between radiation emitted from Jupiter and that received from the Sun. Observations from Earth had earlier shown that Jupiter is hot enough to emit more heat than it receives. The infrared radiometer provides a more accurate measurement of Jupiter's net heat energy output.

The two-channel radiometer (Figure 4-11) measures infrared radiation in the 14 to 25 and 25 to 56 micrometer wavelength regions of the spectrum. The instrument not only determines the temperature across the disc of Jupiter, but also provides important information to aid in determining the thermal structure and chemical composition of the Jovian atmosphere.

Like the ultraviolet photometer, the infrared radiometer uses a fixed telescope that scans the surface of the Jovian cloud tops as the spacecraft spins about its axis. Because of the fixed viewing angle, the infrared instrument could view the planet only for 80 minutes before the time of closest approach.

Designed with a 7.6 cm (3 inch) diameter Cassegrain optical system, the instrument relies upon 88 element, thin film, bi-metallic, thermopiles to detect infrared radiation. Its field of view is approximately 725 by 2400 km (450 by 1500 miles) on Jupiter's cloud surface at the time of closest approach.

Celestial Mechanics Experiment

Principal investigator for this experiment is John D. Anderson, Jet Propulsion Laboratory; his coinvestigator, George W. Null of that Laboratory. Deep space tracking of the Pioneer spacecraft determines its velocity along the Earth-spacecraft line to a fraction of a millimeter per second. This

Figure 4-11. Infrared radiation from Jupiter provides information on cloud temperature and the output of heat from the planet in general. It is measured with this infrared radiometer.

information is obtained once per minute during tracking periods.

The two-way Doppler tracking data, augmented by optical and radar position data about Jupiter, are used to determine the mass of the planet from its perturbations on the path of the spacecraft. Computer calculations, based on the spacecraft's trajectory and known planet and satellite orbital characteristics, provided a five-fold improvement in the accuracy of calculation of Jupiter's mass. Masses of the four large satellites, Io, Europa, Ganymede, and Callisto were also determined to an accuracy of one percent. The experiment determined the polar flattening of Jupiter to within one half mile, and provided data to estimate the mass of surface layers of Jupiter should they exist.

The experiment makes use of the spacecraft itself as a sensitive instrument affected by the gravitational field of Jupiter and its large satellites (Figure 4-12).

Occultation Experiment

The radio signals from the spacecraft were used in another experiment to probe the atmosphere of

58

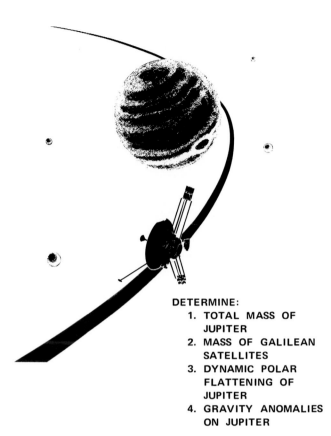

DETERMINE:
1. TOTAL MASS OF JUPITER
2. MASS OF GALILEAN SATELLITES
3. DYNAMIC POLAR FLATTENING OF JUPITER
4. GRAVITY ANOMALIES ON JUPITER

Figure 4-12. A celestial mechanics experiment determined the total mass of Jupiter, the masses of the Galilean satellites, and the polar flattening of Jupiter.

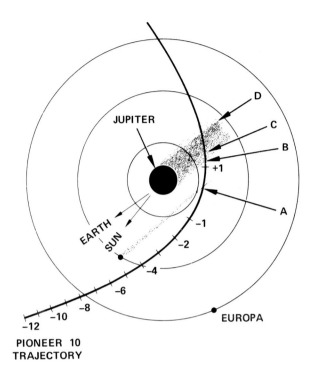

PIONEER 10
TRAJECTORY

A	ENTER IO OCCULTATION	6:41:45 PST
	EXIT IO OCCULTATION	6:43:16 PST
B	ENTER JUPITER OCCULTATION	7:42:25 PST
C	ENTER SUN SHADOW	8:15:35 PST
D	EXIT JUPITER OCCULTATION	8:47:21 PST

Figure 4-13. As the spacecraft flies behind Io and Jupiter, its radio signals are interrupted by the ionosphere and then cut off by the surface of Io and the dense deep atmosphere of Jupiter. But in probing through the atmosphere of these distant bodies the radio signals carry valuable information to scientists back on Earth. Structure, temperature, composition, and charged particles, can all be calculated from the effects of the atmosphere on the radio signals.

Jupiter and its satellite Io (Figure 4-13). Principal investigator for this experiment is Arvydas J. Kliore, Jet Propulsion Laboratory; his coinvestigators are Gunnar Fjeldbo, Dan L. Cain, and Boris L. Seidel of that Laboratory, and S. Ichtiaque Rasool, NASA Headquarters, Washington, D.C.

Passage of the spacecraft's S-band radio signal through Jupiter's atmosphere for about one hour as each Pioneer swung behind the planet probed Jupiter's ionosphere and provided information on the density of the atmosphere to a pressure level of about one Earth's atmosphere.

Similar analyses have been made from the Earth with the light of stars occulted by Jupiter, but Pioneer's S-band telemetry is a more precisely known signal source and provided measurements of a higher order of accuracy. Refraction of the radio signal provided measurement of the electron density of Jupiter's ionosphere and, used in conjunc-

tion with temperature measurements, allowed inferences to be made about the hydrogen/helium ratio in the atmosphere of the giant planet.

Experimenters were also able to measure the absorption profile of the Jovian atmosphere and thereby calculate its abundance of ammonia.

As the spacecraft swung behind Io, similar experiments were made to seek out and examine any atmosphere of that satellite. Io is of particular interest because it appears to affect the radio waves emitted by Jupiter itself.

59

Figure 4-14. A special instrument observed the faint flows in interplanetary space of the Zodiacal Light, the Gegenschein, and the integrated starlight. At Jupiter this same instrument was used to look at the reflective properties of the Jovian atmosphere and of satellites and to build up spin-scan images of these bodies.

Imaging Photopolarimetry Experiment

Principal investigator for this experiment is Tom Gehrels, University of Arizona, Tucson. Coinvestigators are Charles Blenman, Jr., Arthur Clements, Jyrki Hämeen-Anttila, Charles E. KenKnight, William Swindell, and Martin Tomasko, all of the same University; David L. Coffeen, Goddard Institute for Space Studies, New York City; Robert F. Hummer, Santa Barbara Research Center; and Jerry Weinberg and Martha Hanner of the Space Astronomy Laboratory, State University of New York, Albany.

The instrument used for this experiment (Figure 4-14), which is described in detail in Appendix 1, is an imaging photopolarimeter (IPP) which operates in three different modes, differing mainly in their sensitivity and instantaneous field of view.

The most sensitive mode is used during the interplanetary phase of Pioneer's mission to measure the Zodiacal Light, Gegenschein (also called counterglow), and integrated starlight from the Galaxy. This mode was not used at encounter. The other two modes gathered photometric and polarimetric data on Jupiter over a wide range of phase angles and distances, to provide new knowledge about the shape, size, and refractive index of cloud particles, and the abundance of gas above the clouds. The photometric mode also provided data that was processed by computer into images of the planet.

The imaging experiment relies upon the spin of the spacecraft to sweep a small telescope across the planet in narrow strips only 0.03 degrees wide, looking at the planet in red and blue light. These strips were then processed to build up a visual image of the planet.

5

First into the Outer Solar System

THE FIRST PUBLIC discussion of the experiments for the Jupiter mission was announced in a press release addressed to Bay Area Editors: On Thursday, May 7 [1970], the 13 experimenters participating in the first mission to Jupiter will be at NASA's Ames Research Center, Mountain View, for a project coordination meeting. The Pioneer F and G scientific spacecraft now are scheduled for launch to the vicinity of Jupiter in 1972 and 1973. At 11:30 a.m. we will present a review and question and answer session for news media on the mission and experiments.

Several hundred scientists and engineers crowded the main auditorium of the Ames Administration Building . . . a planning session for trajectories to Jupiter aimed at a launch date in early 1972. Questions raised by scientists in connection with their experiments were pondered by celestial dynamicists and spacecraft engineers.

"The ultraviolet experiment needs to look at the sunlit side of the planet."

"It would be important to look at the solar wind outside the ecliptic plane. Could the trajectory to Jupiter provide for this?"

"Can Pioneer reach the region of space, perhaps 30 to 100 times the Earth's distance from the Sun, where the solar wind stops blowing?"

"Does 15 times the Earth's distance from the Sun represent the limit of communication with Pioneer?"

These and other questions sparked this first of a series of coordination meetings to plan the mission to Jupiter. It was stressed that one of the prime purposes of the Pioneer Jupiter mission was to provide information on the environment near the major planet of the Solar System so as to be able to plan more sophisticated spacecraft for later missions to the outer planets.

Among matters debated by scientists was whether or not a passage over a pole of Jupiter would be fruitful since the atmosphere seemed to be more transparent over the poles of the planet. Hence, Pioneer might be able to look down into the 137,000 km (86,000 miles) diameter ball of hydrogen and see much deeper than by a passage over equatorial regions. This, too, was abandoned for the first Pioneer because the spacecraft mission was directed at the radiation belts which were believed to be concentrated about the equatorial regions.

Considerable discussion took place at this and other early meetings about the effects the nuclear powered Radioisotope Thermoelectric Generators (RTGs) might have on the scientific instruments. Pioneer Jupiter was designed as an electromagnetically clean spacecraft so as to be able to measure very weak fields in deep space. The radiation from the RTGs could "dirty" the spacecraft with neutrons and subatomic particles. Representatives of the Atomic Energy Commission explained how elimination of impurities from the radioactive fuel elements could reduce the radiation hazard from the RTGs and how this was being planned.

At a press conference following the technical meetings, the exploratory and ambitious nature of the Jupiter mission was emphasized. The duration of flight would be greater than that for any other space project to date. There were tremendous unknown factors in the environmental hazards between Mars and Jupiter and in close approach to Jupiter itself. Moreover, as pointed out by Glenn A. Reiff, Pioneer Program Manager from NASA Headquarters: "The telecommunications network will be stretched to the limits of its capabilities."

Charles F. Hall, Project Manager at NASA-Ames, confirmed that all the spacecraft design had been completed and that construction of the first of the two spacecraft was under way at TRW Systems, Redondo Beach, California. "Experimenters and staffs are here to discuss the design of the scientific equipment to integrate with the spacecraft and its mission profile." Everything was on schedule, said Mr. Hall, as he pointed out how important it was to keep to the tight schedule, since the launch window would be open for only 18 days in 1972.

Almost a year later, in March 1971, at a similar meeting held in the main auditorium at TRW Systems, scientists stated that the RTGs were generating higher radiation than expected at the May 1970 meeting, but instruments had been adapted to this radiative environment. Details of the science experiments showed the wealth of data expected from the mission in space and at Jupiter. Scientific equipment, like the spacecraft, were being readied on schedule, even though the scientists had to make many guesses at what conditions would be like in the asteroid belt and at Jupiter. Thus, instruments had to be designed with a wide range of capabilities because of extremely sparse information about the outer Solar System.

Meanwhile, trajectory analysts continued their work and evaluated various approaches to the

planet. Targeting to have the spacecraft occulted by a satellite of Jupiter would allow the radio signals to probe through any atmosphere possessed by the satellite and determine its composition. Questions revolved on which satellite. Io was a prime objective for such an experiment because somehow it modulates the radio waves from Jupiter itself. But the other satellites were also of interest to scientists as potentially possessing atmospheres.

On November 16, 1971, Ralph W. Holtzclaw, Spacecraft Systems Manager at NASA-Ames, discussed the needs to make the spacecraft reliable for its long mission. "No single component failure can be catastrophic to the mission," he said.

Mr. Holtzclaw pointed out that the Pioneer mission is quite different from earlier space missions. Scientists have to spend several years planning the experiments. Then the spacecraft operates for seven or eight years more in space, possibly for even longer. Scientists are thus being asked to dedicate 10 years or more of their lives to a single experiment.

All the preparations went well. From contract award to the scheduled launch date, early March 1972, was 1 month less than 2-1/2 years. But the thousands of people involved in the Pioneer Jupiter program performed their tasks on schedule to meet the critical time of launch window (Figure 5-1).

Charles F. Hall praised those who had made the program possible: "It is most appropriate to compliment the many dedicated people who have worked so hard to reach this first goal of the Pioneer F mission to Jupiter and to congratulate all for a job well done. I estimate that at the time of the Pioneer F launch, more than 15 million man-hours will have been expended to make this goal possible. I am sure that you all feel as I do that a successful mission wherein we will be exploring new frontiers in space will be a just compensation

Figure 5-1. Many thousands of people contributed to the development and fabrication of the Pioneer spacecraft destined for the Jupiter mission. Their dedication made it possible to meet the tight schedule for the first available launch window.

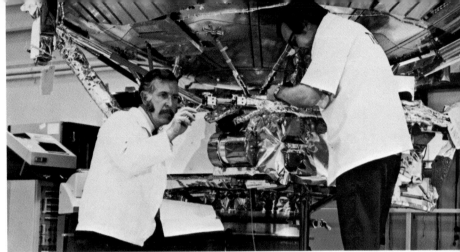
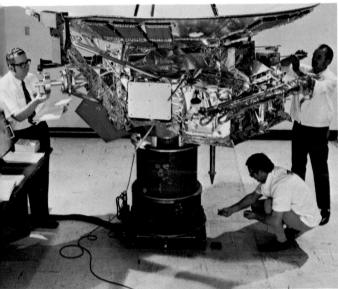

DR. F. B. McDONALD   DR. J. A. VAN ALLEN   DR. J. A. SIM

for this large effort and that we are, indeed, a fortunate, select group which has been given the opportunity to participate in and contribute to the Pioneer F Mission."

By December 22, 1971, the Atlas Centaur launch vehicle stood ready on Launch Complex 36A at the John F. Kennedy Space Center, Florida. The spacecraft was airlifted with its full complement of scientific instruments, but without its RTGs, from TRW Systems, California, to Florida on January 15, 1972.

To ensure operational readiness of the spacecraft and its science instruments for launch, it was tested through a simulated countdown in Building A0 (Figure 5-2). The RTGs were installed and the spacecraft loaded with propellant and, finally, mated to the third stage of the launch vehicle and encapsulated. The whole assembly was then transferred to the launch pad and mated to the Atlas-Centaur.

Yet when the spacecraft was ready on its launch pad, all was not smooth sailing. Upper atmosphere winds delayed the launch after the window opened on February 27, 1972.

Within 59 minutes of the planned 8:52 p.m. liftoff, blockhouse electrical power failed. Then, high winds made it too hazardous to launch the spacecraft. These winds prevented launching on February 28 and March 1, and it was not until March 2, 1972, at 8:49 p.m. EST, that the Atlas-Centaur lifted from the launch pad (Figure 5-3) carrying Earth's first space probe to the outer planets. The beauty of a night launching from Cape Kennedy was punctuated and enhanced by distant thunder and by lightning flashing on the cloud tops as the brilliant light of the Atlas engines' exhaust jet rose through the clouds.

Events happened fast and forced quick decisions. Mission controllers had to know if the spacecraft was affected in any way by the stresses upon it. Telemetered data poured into the control centers by radio from the launch vehicle and the spacecraft. If anything looked awry, corrective action had to be taken immediately to try to

Figure 5-2. A simulated countdown at Kennedy Space Center thoroughly checked the spacecraft prior to launching.

Figure 5-3. Finally, at 8:49 p.m., 2 March, 1972, Pioneer 10 started its journey to Jupiter and thence to the stars.

64

save the spacecraft and its scientific payload. But atop the powerful Atlas-Centaur booster, Pioneer 10 withstood the pounding thrust of the rocket engines while it absorbed enough kinetic energy to break free from Earth's gravitational fetters.

Powered flight lasted some 17 minutes, accelerating the spacecraft to 51,682 km (32,114 miles) an hour, almost 11,300 km (7,000 miles) per hour faster than any previous man-made object. The Atlas exhausted its propellants and dropped behind as the white brilliance of the Centaur took over the thrusting into space. But the tiny ball of brilliant white fire began to disappear into the black void of the night sky. Soon it was lost to view of the people on the beaches, lost to view of Earthmen as a tangible thing. The spacecraft was on its way to Jupiter, and onwards to infinity, for it will ultimately escape from our Solar System and journey among the distant stars. Successfully on its path to the giant planet, Pioneer F became Pioneer 10.

Shortly after separation from the upper stages, the spacecraft deployed its RTG power units at the end of two arms, thereby slowing its rate of rotation. Then the third boom, tipped with the sensitive magnetometer, crept slowly out to its full 5.2 meter (17 foot) length.

Launching achieved unprecedented accuracy, requiring a correction of only 50.4 km (31.3 miles) per hour to the launch velocity. This correction was commanded and took place on March 7. Actually, Pioneer could have reached Jupiter, but the correction was needed to obtain a time of arrival that would better suit some of the experiments.

After Pioneer 10 had separated from its launch vehicle, a sequencer activated the attitude control system to turn the spacecraft around and orient it for its long voyage so that the big dish antenna pointed toward Earth. Actually, while near to Earth, Pioneer 10's orientation was such that sunlight illuminated it from the side, thus causing heating problems for several weeks after launch. To reduce these temperature problems, the spacecraft

Figure 5-4. Only 11 hours after launch Pioneer 10 passed the orbit of the Moon, shown conceptually in this artist's sketch. Actually the Moon was at a more distant part of its orbit.

was, in fact, commanded to point slightly away from Earth so that a shadow of the dish antenna would shield vulnerable parts, such as the battery, from solar heat.

Pioneer 10 passed the orbit of the Moon in less than 11 hours after launch (Figure 5-4).

The plasma analyzer was the only instrument carried by Pioneer 10 designed to look directly at the Sun. Most others could not point sunward without risking serious damage. So, in the early stages of the flight, when the Sun illuminated the spacecraft from the side, some of the instruments were left unenergized while others were protected in various ways, such as by sunlight screens.

Instruments such as the magnetometer and charged particle detectors are not affected by sunlight. They were turned on quickly to provide an in-flight calibration in the well-explored magnetic and radiation environment of space surrounding the Earth.

Two days after liftoff, the cosmic ray telescope was turned on, and then in the next few following days, the ultraviolet photometer, the asteroid-meteoroid detector, imaging photopolarimeter, and the plasma analyzer, in that order. All scientific instruments had been turned on by 10 days after launch.

Scientists, located at the Pioneer Mission Operations Center, watched each instrument closely, as

Figure 5-5. A first task was to investigate the Zodiacal Light, a faint
glow seen in dark Earth skies after sunset and before sunrise.

commands were sent to turn on each of the scientific instruments onboard the spacecraft. The operations science chief for Pioneer, the cognizant instrument engineer, and the principal investigator for the respective science instruments, inspected the returned data, critically seeking any information that might reveal an instrument malfunction that required corrective action. All went well with Pioneer 10; all the science experiments survived the stress of the launch.

After the first month of its journey, the performance of Pioneer 10 continued to be excellent. As Ralph W. Holtzclaw said at the time: "Now that we have had a chance to recover from the emotional trauma of getting Pioneer 10 launched, it is time to sit down and perform a factual engineering examination of this machine 'we' have wrought. As Pioneer 10 settles into the 'cruise' phase of its voyage to Jupiter, many analyses must be made of the live operation of this vehicle in a space environment — to ensure specified performance during the crucial Jupiter encounter. Preliminary indications are that Pioneer 10 is a good spacecraft and a good mission."

Ninety-seven days after launch, Pioneer 10 had covered one seventh of the time of the mission to Jupiter and one quarter of the distance. There had been a few anomalies within the spacecraft, but nothing serious. Experimenters were enthusiastic about the way equipment behaved. The characteristics of charged particles, the interplanetary plasma, the Zodiacal Light, had all been observed and studied in detail.

Project scientists announced some preliminary findings of Pioneer 10 as it crossed the orbit of Mars and headed out into unexplored space. Said Charles F. Hall: "This meeting today is to cover the passage of the Pioneer spacecraft into a new area. By tomorrow we will have crossed a point farther from the Sun than the farthest distance of Mars. From now on, we will be in a new area of space."

So far the explorer had been "East of the Mississippi," but on crossing the most distant point of the orbit of Mars, it became a true pioneer into the unknown. Here the solar wind was expected to change dramatically. Here, the flux of small particles might build up to damaging proportions in the asteroid belt. Here, the spacecraft signals became weaker and the time of command and action began to increase. The controllers and the scientists were gaining experience in controlling very distant spacecraft, a learning process of anticipating and doing things in advance.

The imaging photopolarimeter, the instrument that would later in the mission provide data to build up photographic quality images of Jupiter and perhaps one of its satellites, had been busy investigating the Zodiacal Light. If one looks at the sky from Earth on a moonless night (Figure 5-5). away from the glare of city lights, a very faint glow is seen over the whole of the sky, but concentrated near to the path of the Sun through the celestial sphere, along the constellations of the Zodiac. In spring, in the northern hemisphere, this Zodiacal Light is most easily seen as a cone of light in the western sky, after the sky has darkened at sunset; and in autumn, this cone precedes the rising of the Sun in the East.

Pioneer 10 measured the intensity of the Zodiacal Light in interplanetary space, and for the first time investigated, away from Earth, a concentration of the Zodiacal Light in a direction away from the Sun. This anti-solar concentration is called the Gegenschein or counterglow. Although the prevailing scientific opinion was that this glow results from sunlight scattered by interplanetary particles there was some speculation that the Gegenschein might somehow be connected with the Earth, possibly a reflection from a tail of particles streaming out away from the Sun. But Pioneer 10 showed that the Gegenschein still shines as far as Mars and confirmed that it is not an Earth-related phenomenon.

Now a further correction was needed to get the spacecraft precisely to Jupiter for an observation of a satellite. Said Charles F. Hall, "If we don't make any further correction to the trajectory, we [the spacecraft] will not be occulted by Io. We are in error by 14 minutes at the arrival. Our plan is to correct at the end of June or by mid-July. We have waited this long because there is a pressure on the spacecraft due to light energy coming from the Sun. We wanted to allow the spacecraft to coast for a long period of time so we can accurately determine just what this solar pressure is."

On July 15, 1972, Pioneer 10 became the first spacecraft to enter the asteroid belt. Since the belt is too thick to fly over without prohibitively expensive launch vehicles, all missions to the outer planets must fly through it.

Based on a variety of analyses, project officials expected a safe passage, but the risk was always present that analyses from Earth could be wrong. Pioneer's closest approach to any of the known asteroids, visible by telescope, was 8.8 million km (5.5 million miles). One was a 1 km (1/2 mile) diameter asteroid on August 2, and the other was Nike 24 km (15 miles) in diameter on December 2, 1972.

But any particle over 0.05 cm (1/50 inch) in diameter could seriously damage the Pioneer 10 spacecraft since it could impact with 15 times the speed of a high powered rifle bullet. An estimate of such an impact was one in ten, or a 90 percent chance of passing through the belt undamaged.

Pioneer Jupiter reached 322 million km (200 million miles) from Earth on September 1,

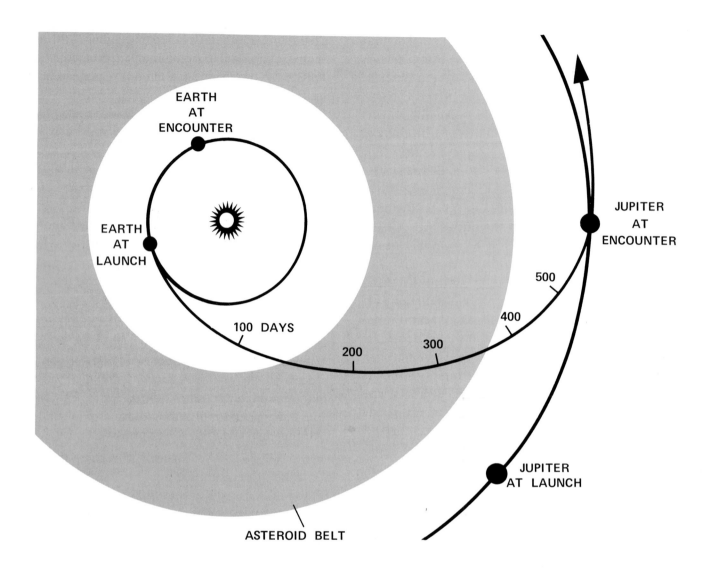

EARTH
AT
ENCOUNTER

EARTH
AT
LAUNCH

100 DAYS

200

300

400

500

JUPITER
AT
ENCOUNTER

JUPITER
AT LAUNCH

ASTEROID BELT

Figure 5-6. Pioneer investigated the concentration of small meteoroids in space, finding that this varies somewhat with distance from the Sun but not entirely as had been expected. Pioneer 10 penetrated the asteroid belt and remained undamaged.

1972, and was then deep in the asteroid belt and still undamaged (Figure 5-6). Now it took controllers 43 minutes to send a signal to the spacecraft and get a reply from it. Ten of the spacecraft's experiments were operating. The remaining experiment was not needed until the spacecraft reached Jupiter, but this infrared radiometer had been turned on monthly to check its operational status.

In August 1972, several unprecedented storms on the Sun (Figure 5-7) provided Pioneer 10 with a

unique opportunity to measure the behavior of the solar wind at much greater interplanetary distances than ever before.

Known as region 331, a huge area of the Sun unexpectedly erupted to produce three enormous storms on August 2 and another on August 7. This latter event produced in one hour enough energy to satisfy the present rate of electrical power consumption of the United States for 100 million years.

Effects of the storm in Canada, the northern United States, Sweden, and Alaska were severe since the solar wind warped the Earth's magnetic field and caused power and communications blackouts and other magnetic disturbances.

Pioneer 10's measurements were correlated with those from a series of earlier Pioneers in orbit around the Sun. These four spacecraft, Pioneers 6, 7, 8, and 9, are located at different azimuthal positions from Earth, but at solar distances only slightly different from that of Earth. The Pioneers measured the solar wind and its magnetic fields as it swept through space (Figure 5-8). Pioneer 9, close to Earth, saw the highest solar wind speeds ever recorded: 3,597,000 km (2,235,000 miles) per hour. But in crossing the 214 million km (133 million miles) to Pioneer 10 in just 76 hours, the wind slowed to about half this velocity.

Pioneer 10 measured the enormous equivalent temperature of 2 million degrees Kelvin, similar to that of the solar corona itself.

Dr. John Wolfe, Pioneer Project Scientist, explained: "The velocity of the solar wind in the interplanetary medium is dependent on the temperature of the solar corona, and from a temperature point of view, the solar corona is quite inhomogeneous. Thus, the Sun emits both fast and slow flowing plasma. The energy density of the solar wind is 100 times that of the interplanetary magnetic field, so the solar wind drags along and carries the magnetic field with it. This magnetic field not only screens incoming cosmic rays and prevents the low energy ones from outside the Solar System from entering into the inner Solar System, but also stops the fast flowing plasmas from penetrating the slow flowing plasmas.

"Because the Sun rotates, a fast solar wind can catch up with a slow solar wind. When the fast and slow winds interact, they produce a snowplow effect and steep gradients are produced at the interface. These gradients scatter incoming cosmic rays. One of the missions of Pioneer 10 is to check where these cosmic ray scattering regions might fade away, perhaps at 10 to 15 times the distance of Earth from the Sun; way beyond the orbit of Jupiter."

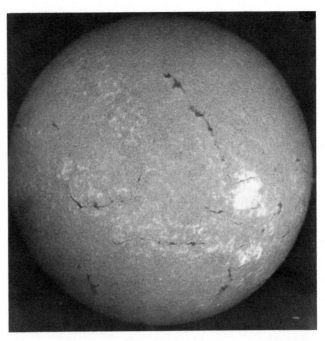

Figure 5-7. In August 1972 an unprecedented event on the Sun provided Pioneer 10 with a unique opportunity to observe the solar wind. A series of immense flares erupted on the Sun and sprayed interplanetary space with highly energetic particles. (*Photo: NOAA*)

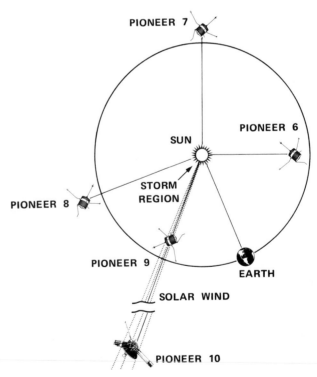

Figure 5-8. Pioneer 10, operating in conjunction with other Pioneer spacecraft closer to Earth, observed the distribution of the solar wind from these immense flares.

Since the only star that man can study at close range is the Sun, the data from Pioneer 10 is expected to help in man's understanding of all Sun-like stars.

Up to the point half way through the asteroid belt, Pioneer 10 still proceeded undamaged. It passed through the two regions of greatest asteroid density — at 400 million km (250 million miles) and 480 million km (300 million miles) from the Sun — unscathed, although sightings of larger asteroid particles appeared to increase in number for about a week near to the 400 million km (250 million mile) region.

In February 1973, Pioneer 10 at last officially emerged from the asteroid belt, at a distance of 550 million km (340 million miles) from the Sun, having completed the 435 million km (270 million mile), seven-month passage through the belt without incident. Pioneer showed that the belt appeared to contain much less material in the small particle sizes than had been anticipated. The way was open to exploration of the outer Solar System.

As Pioneer 10 emerged from the asteroid belt, Pioneer G, its follow-on spacecraft, was readied for launch at Kennedy Space Center. Should Pioneer 10 in any way fail during the rest of the mission, Pioneer G would repeat the failed part of the mission. Otherwise, Pioneer G would be retargeted to fly a different course through the Jovian environment and obtain another set of samples of that environment.

The first launch window opened at 9:00 p.m. on April 5, 1973. A few seconds later, Pioneer G was successfully launched to become Pioneer 11 (Figure 5-9). Subsequent hours proved tense when one of the RTG booms failed to extend properly. However, the trouble was corrected, and Pioneer 11 followed its sister ship toward Jupiter: all systems working properly, all scientific instruments performing well, and additionally, with an improved star sensor.

Pioneer 11 repeated the experiments of Pioneer 10 in the interplanetary mission and like Pioneer 10, it too passed safely through the asteroid belt. Pioneer 11 was targeted to be closest to Jupiter at 9:21 p.m. PST on December 2, 1974, and then to fly on to the planet Saturn, for a rendezvous with the ringed planet in September 1979 to seek information about that mysterious planet before a more sophisticated spacecraft, Mariner Jupiter-Saturn, arrives there several months later.

At the beginning of November 1973, controllers entered the busiest activity period connected with Pioneer 10. They readied the spacecraft for its time of closest approach with Jupiter, early in December. By November 6, long range imaging tests commenced on the planet at a distance of 25 million km (15.5 million miles). And Pioneer 10 crossed the orbit of Jupiter's outermost satellite, Hades, on November 8. Controllers were now in the process of starting the sequence of sending some 16,000 commands to the spacecraft to direct all the various scientific experiments and the spacecraft for the 60-day encounter period during which Pioneer 10 made its close passage to within 130,354 km (81,000 miles) of Jupiter's cloud tops on December 3, 1973.

Figure 5-9. Pioneer 11 followed Pioneer 10 toward Jupiter on April 5, 1973. Launching took place within a few seconds of the opening of the launch window.

70

The mission had by now set an array of records:

* Pioneer 10, the first NASA spacecraft to use all nuclear electrical power, had traveled farther and faster than any other man-made object. Its launch speed of 51,682 km (32,114 miles) per hour, a record in itself, was, however, soon to be surpassed by its speed at closest approach to Jupiter of 132,000 km (82,000 miles) per hour.

* Pioneer 10 had communicated many times farther than ever before, and held promise of communicating to the immense distance of Uranus' orbit, nearly 3.22 billion km (2 billion miles) from Earth.

* Pioneer 10 was the first spacecraft to fly beyond Mars' orbit; the first to cross the asteroid belt; and would become the first man-made object to escape our Solar System.

Moreover, the accuracy of the control was such that Pioneer 10 was expected to reach its closest approach to Jupiter within one minute of the planned time: one minute in almost two years of flight.

Shifts of people maintained watch on Pioneer 10 around the clock for the several weeks of close approach and passage through the Jovian system (Figure 5-10). They included experts on the spacecraft subsystems and on the scientific instruments, not only project personnel but also experimenter personnel and even a trained volunteer (H. H. Dodeck) from Germany's HELIOS project.

By November 29, 1973, with all systems aboard the spacecraft functioning perfectly, Pioneer 10 had crossed the orbits of all seven outermost satellites of the Jovian system and was readying for its plunge toward the radiation belts and its close encounter with the giant planet. Dr. Hans Mark, Director of the Ames Research Center, told newsmen gathered in the auditorium at Ames for the

Figure 5-10. Shifts of people maintained watch on Pioneer 10 around the clock for the several weeks of encounter with Jupiter.

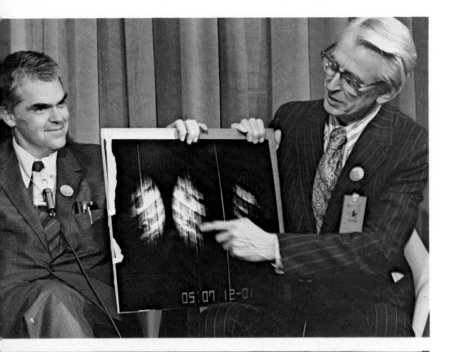

Figure 5-11. NASA Administrator Dr. James C. Fletcher and Ames Research Center Director, Dr. Hans Mark, brief newsmen and visiting scientists gathered in the auditorium at NASA-Ames Research Center to hear updated accounts of the events from experimenters and project personnel.

historic Jupiter encounter (Figure 5-11): "This is an unusual event. The planet Jupiter, as you know, is an object that has been the subject of fairly extensive investigation for almost 400 years. Galileo, who looked at the planet through his primitive telescope in 1610, discovered ... the four brilliant moons that surround the planet. This observation provided, I think, the first really visceral proof, as it were, that the Copernican model of the Solar System wasn't exactly the way it looks. Jupiter, therefore, served, perhaps, the function of quite profoundly changing the way we think about ourselves and the way we think about the universe."

Charles F. Hall added: "We are really only twelve generations away from Galileo and his first crude look at the planet. Twelve generations later, we are actually there measuring many of the characteristics of the planet itself" (Figure 5-12).

Pioneer 10 had, by now, already passed through the bow shock where Jupiter's magnetic field affects the solar wind. This took place about noon on November 26, at a distance of about 108.9 Jupiter radii or about 6.4 million km (4 million miles), a little farther out than had been anticipated. A first indication that the spacecraft had crossed the shock wave was instruments sensing approximately a 50 percent drop in solar wind speed. This information, of course, arrived at Earth 45 minutes after the spacecraft measured the drop in velocity. Prior to the shock, the solar wind blew on the spacecraft at 451 km (280 miles) per second. Immediately after crossing the shock, this wind dropped to about 225 km (140 miles) per second, while its temperature rose from about 50,000 degrees Kelvin to a half million degrees. Of course the spacecraft, itself, did not experience this temperature which was that of a highly rarefied plasma unable to transfer significant quantities of heat to the spacecraft.

A day later — November 27, 1973, at noon — Pioneer 10 crossed the boundary between the shocked solar wind and the magnetic field of Jupiter, called the magnetopause. The distance was now 96.4 Jupiter radii. Explained Dr. John Wolfe (Figure 5-13): "The observation is that this is the point at which the pressure of gas coming from the Sun, after it has gone through the shock wave, becomes equal to the pressure of Jupiter's magnetic field, and the gas which is contained within that field. So the solar wind stopped at this point."

While similar to Earth, this environment of Jupiter was in some ways quite different. Near the boundary of Earth's magnetic field, all the strength that holds off the solar wind is due to the Earth's magnetic field. But for Jupiter, this turns out not to be true. Much plasma is contained within Jupiter's magnetic field near the boundary, and helps to hold off the solar wind. This additional barrier is about equal to the magnetic field itself. Another point discovered is that the magnetopause is close to the bow shock.

Pioneer 10's instruments confirmed what radio astronomers had postulated about the magnetic field of Jupiter, that it is inverted, compared to that of the Earth. The magnetic north pole is to the south. The science experiments showed, too, that the magnetosphere of Jupiter is somewhat different from that of the Earth, being flattened in its outer regions. This was inferred by the way Jupiter's magnetic field lines were stretched out from the planet in the outer regions. The magnetic field of Jupiter is offset from the axis of rotation so that at any point in space, around the planet, the field appears to move up and down; the disc of the outer magnetosphere wobbles relative to the surrounding space.

As for the spacecraft, none of the redundant circuits had yet been needed. So optimism was high that even if the Jupiter passage did damage some equipment, there would still be backup equipment available for the post encounter period of flight beyond Jupiter.

The spacecraft had, however, speeded up slightly over its anticipated course and was to arrive at Jupiter one minute earlier than previously calculated. This arose because Jupiter turned out to be slightly heavier than calculated from Earth-based observations.

Figure 5-12. Twelve generations after Galileo's first telescopic look at Jupiter, we are actually there making measurements (Charles F. Hall).

Figure 5-13. Dr. John Wolfe explains observations made by Pioneer 10 as it traverses the Jovian system.

73

In the previous 24 days, thousands of commands had been transmitted to the spacecraft and during that time, only one ground data system failure occurred, when one of the computers became overloaded. Recovery was within two minutes. The numbers of commands were, by this time, building up daily from 400 to 2,000 per day as the closest approach to Jupiter neared. A special command sequence was developed to reconfigure the imaging photopolarimeter regardless of what spurious command functions were activated by the radiation. Also, a sequence of contingency commands was periodically transmitted so that the spacecraft could be corrected even before the signals telling of the spurious commands could be received at Earth.

During the encounter, only one scientific objective was missed because of false commands generated by Jupiter's intense radiation. This was the close-in imaging of the satellite Io. The imaging photopolarimeter responded to spurious commands 10 times, but the reconfiguration countered these commands so that only a few partial close-ups of Jupiter were lost, in addition to the Io image.

Pictures of Jupiter had now been coming back for several days, each one built up from a number of scans as the rotation of the spacecraft swept the imaging photopolarimeter's narrow-angle telescope system across the disc of Jupiter. Twelve pictures of Jupiter were received at Earth on November 26 and many more in subsequent days. Images were returned in two colors, red and blue, from which a detailed color picture of the planet could be produced later.

Quick-look pictures from the spacecraft were displayed on television screens in the auditorium at NASA Ames. As the spacecraft data arrived they were placed vertically on the screen as a series of bars until the complete disc of the planet was assembled.

The Pioneer Image Converter System (PICS) was developed by L. Ralph Baker of the University of Arizona. The system was designed to present real-time display of Pioneer spin-scan images to allow scientists to monitor operation of the imaging photopolarimeter during encounter, and also to provide a video signal so that the images could be displayed to the press and made available to television networks. Thus, the public was able to view the results of the flyby of Jupiter as it took place.

The imaging photopolarimeter on the spacecraft scanned the planet in two colors, red and blue. But these colors, although chosen to get best scientific results from Jupiter, are not sufficient to produce a visually satisfactory image. If the red and blue images from Pioneer 10 had been simply mixed together, they would have produced a magenta image, unlike Jupiter and unnatural to the human eye. Instead, the red and blue signals were mixed to make a synthetic green signal, and a normal three-color combination was then obtained (Figure 5-14).

To begin with, the displayed pictures were pictures of Jupiter similar to those taken from Earth. This was because, with the spacecraft far from the planet, there was little distortion. But as the spacecraft sped towards the Jovian cloud tops, the rapidly changing geometry made the disc of Jupiter look like a painting of the planet on a rubber sheet which had then been stretched out of shape. Even so, the visible details (Figure 5-15) held tremendous promise for the time when these close-in pictures could later be processed and corrected by the computers, as described in later chapters. The PICS system has been improved to remove some of this distortion for the Pioneer 11 encounter. For this real-time display of images of Jupiter, the Pioneer Program received an EMMY award (Figure 5-16).

By December 2, 1973, the imaging of Jupiter began to exceed the best pictures obtained previously from Earth. When Pioneer 10 approached to six times the radius of Jupiter and still functioned well, it had cleared the way for the 1977 Mariner Jupiter-Saturn mission, as this would be the planned closest approach for that mission.

But Pioneer 10 explored farther down into the hostile environment of Jupiter, to two Jupiter radii

74

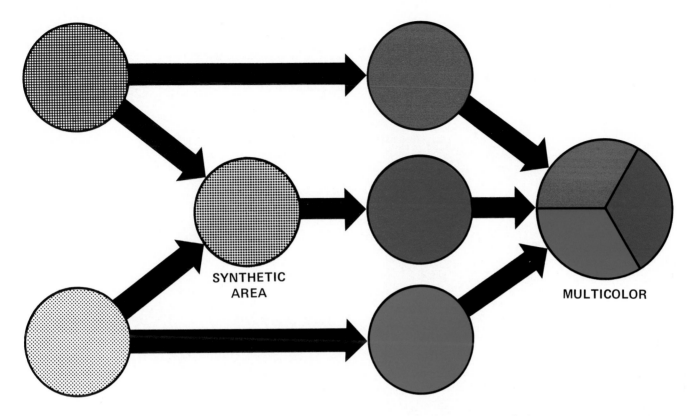

SYNTHETIC
AREA

MULTICOLOR

Figure 5-14. A Pioneer Image Converter System allowed scientists and the public to see images of Jupiter almost as quickly as they were received at Earth. Color images of Jupiter were built up for display as they were received at Pioneer Mission Operations Center. Not only could scientists monitor the quality of the experiment during encounter, but also the images provided the public with a first-hand view of the large planet as Pioneer flew by Jupiter. The Pioneer Image Converter System (PICS) produced a synthetic green image of Jupiter to mix with the blue and red images returned from Pioneer and provide a reasonable color rendition that was also suitable for public television.

Figure 5-16. For the real-time display and release to the media of Jupiter images, the Pioneer Program received an EMMY award.

Figure 5-15. Excitement rose as the PICS system displayed images of Jupiter of ever increasing size as Pioneer 10 plunged in at high speed toward its closest approach to the planet. But perhaps the most dramatic moment was after encounter and the spacecraft had been hidden behind Jupiter. PICS started to show a few spots which gradually built up into a very distorted crescent Jupiter. "Sunrise on Jupiter," an experimenter exclaimed excitedly. "We've made it safely through periapsis." Subsequent PICS images showed a crescent Jupiter which gradually decreased in size. (See following pages.)

above the cloud tops. In the words of Robert Kraemer of NASA Headquarters: "We can say that we sent Pioneer 10 off to tweak a dragon's tail, and it did that and more. It gave it a really good yank and . . . it [Pioneer 10] managed to survive."

Some spacecraft systems began to feel the effect of the Jovian radiation environment. One of the investigators used up 99 percent of the range on his instrument to obtain data despite the radiation, but the instrument made it through the encounter with just the remaining one percent to spare.

As expected, some of the instruments had saturated in the intense radiation field close to Jupiter. Two of the interplanetary cosmic ray detectors saturated a day before the closest encounter. Scientists had planned for this and provided a special Jovian radiation belt detector which worked well. Protons were measured for the first time in the radiation environment of the giant planet.

The interplanetary electron measuring instrument also saturated on the way in, but again, the experimenters were ready with a pair of special detectors for the Jovian environment to measure successfully the close-in electrons and protons.

All experimenters experienced anxious hours as telemetered data showed their detectors climbing towards the limits. They breathed sighs of relief as peaks were reached, and the intensities measured began to drop.

Up until noontime of December 3, as the Pioneer 10 approached periapsis, all went well with the imaging photopolarimeter. Many thousand commands had been sent successfully. Then about 10:00 a.m., at a distance of nine Jupiter radii, the instrument started to act as though it had received spurious commands which upset the imaging sequence. The problem was quickly overcome, but it occurred again on the way out from Jupiter at about the same distance.

Nevertheless, the equipment obtained close-in images of the terminator and the Great Red Spot. But then Pioneer 10 went behind Jupiter and communication with Earth ceased. Anxiously, the experimenters waited for the return of the signals. Would all the scientific instruments continue work-

78

ing after the the radiation bath at closest approach? Lyn R. Doose, one of the imaging experimenter staff at the University of Arizona, describes the drama of the emergence: "We watched the PICS image displayed in real time as the signals came back from the distant planet. A single bright spot appeared, and then another, until a line gradually built up. We knew we were seeing sunrise on Jupiter as the PICS image showed a crescent-like shape (Figure 5-16). We had survived passage through periapsis: the IPP was still working." The following hours produced more unique crescent images of Jupiter as Pioneer 10 headed away after periapsis.

All other equipment performed as expected. Ultraviolet and infrared scans and meteoroid dust sampling went according to plan.

Commented Robert Kraemer immediately after the close encounter: "The Mission, by all standards, is written down right now as 100 percent successful. It is very hard to see how it [Pioneer 10] could have done its job any better. All elements went beyond the project teams' expectations — getting off to a good launch a couple of years ago, tracking the spacecraft, getting all the data back, has been just a beautiful effort."

The spacecraft contractor's Project Manager from TRW Systems, B. J. O'Brien, commented: "We did see the radiation effects at about the points we predicted . . . the small indications of what failures we had were precisely in those areas we would have predicted, namely the power.

"We feel a little bit like Professor Higgins in Pygmalion who said, 'We did it'."

Project Science Chief, Richard O. Fimmel, commented: "This has been the most exciting day of my life!" Many of the principal investigators agreed wholeheartedly.

Pioneer 10 did what it was supposed to do . . . find out if spacecraft could explore Jupiter despite the hazards of the Jovian environment. Pioneer 10 found out what the environment of Jupiter really is and provided enough new data in itself to whet our appetites for more exploration of the giant planet.

80

Afterwards, Pioneer 10 headed for the outer reaches of the Solar System to cross Saturn's orbit in 1976 and the orbit of Uranus in 1980, where communication will probably soon be lost. By 1983, it crosses the orbit of Pluto and then continues at 40,000 km (25,000 miles) per hour into interstellar space, man's first emissary to the stars.

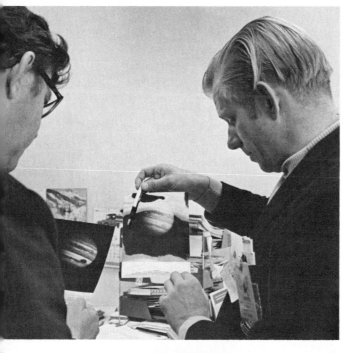

Meanwhile, Pioneer 11 had been following Pioneer 10 for a rendezvous with Jupiter. Severe thunderstorms at the Florida launch site had delayed preparations with a spell of bad weather. But crews at the site made up for the pre-launch delays and had the spacecraft ready for the launch window. The lift-off took place as scheduled at 6:11 p.m. PST on 5 April 1973. The spacecraft separated from the launch vehicle at 6:26 p.m., but as the RTG booms were deployed to slow the spin of the spacecraft and place the radioactive material as far as possible from the body of the spacecraft, trouble arose. One of the booms failed to extend to its full extent. The spacecraft continued to spin at too fast a rate.

Thrusters were fired to cause vibrations and extended the boom slightly. Then the spacecraft was reoriented to prevent excessive solar heating. The boom extended fully and the spin rate adjusted to its correct value of 4.8 rpm. Now all systems were operating correctly on the spacecraft.

On April 11, 1973, the course of the spacecraft was changed slightly by an Earth-line velocity change maneuver. This correction aimed Pioneer 11 to a passage to the right of Jupiter as seen from Earth and about 20,000 km (12,400 mi.) above the cloud tops of the giant planet. This aiming point was chosen to provide several flyby options, including a continued journey beyond Jupiter to Saturn, and allowed the choice of option to be made later in the mission by another maneuver.

With the spacecraft 11 million km (7 million mi.) on its way the solar wind and cosmic ray instruments were sending good data about the interplanetary medium.

Trajectories of Pioneer 10 and Pioneer 11 as seen from the celestial North Pole projected onto the ecliptic plane are shown in Figure 5-16. During encounter with Jupiter the flyby trajectory is such that the speed of Pioneer 11 is almost doubled. The transfer of energy from Jupiter to the spacecraft boosts the speed of the spacecraft as effectively as a rocket engine and flings Pioneer 11

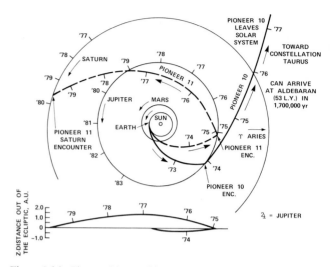

Figure 5-16. Pioneer 10 and 11 heliocentric trajectories. The time ticks shown along the trajectories and planetary orbits represent the distance traveled during each year.

toward the ringed planet Saturn. Pioneer 11's trajectory from Jupiter to Saturn is about three times as long as its path from the Earth to Jupiter. Along this trajectory Pioneer 11 flies high above the plane of the ecliptic, reaching a maximum height of 164 million km (102 million mi.) in the later part of 1976. This flight is the first spacecraft to probe deep space far from the ecliptic plane.

Pioneer 11 completed a safe passage through the asteroid belt on 20 March 1974, emerging unscathed as its predecessor. The experiments on Pioneer 11 confirmed the findings of Pioneer 10. As the spacecraft traveled outward in the Solar System from Earth's orbit, the smallest particles (0.001 mm) detected by the spacecraft's instruments appeared to decline in number. Somewhat larger particles (0.01 to 0.1 mm) seemed to be evenly distributed all the way from Earth's orbit through the asteroid belt itself, with no increase in the belt. Still larger particles (0.1 to 1.0 mm) were found to be three times as frequent in the center of the belt as near Earth.

The modified gas-cell instrument aboard Pioneer 11 found some results different from those of Pioneer 10. Walls of the gas cells on the Pioneer 11 detectors were thicker, so that only particles from 0.02 to 0.1 mm diameter (1/100 millionth to one millionth of a gram) were recorded.

82

For these particles, about half as many more gas-cell penetrations were found near the Earth by Pioneer 11 than by Pioneer 10. This implies about the same number of small and large particles were present. However, between 180 and 344 million km (112 and 214 million mi.) from the Sun Pioneer 11 found a virtual absence of larger particles. Its detector recorded only one penetration. In the asteroid belt, the larger particles appeared again, but only about one sixth as many as in the total range measured by Pioneer 10. This appears to mean that in the asteroid belt smaller particles of 0.01 to 0.1 mm size are three times as common as larger particles.

Between the Earth and the outer edge of the asteroid belt, Pioneer 11 counted 20 penetrations, 7 of them taking place while the spacecraft was within the belt.

The larger asteroidal particles, measured by the asteroid-meteoroid telescope, are mostly in the range of size 0.1 to 1.0 mm diameter, one millionth to one thousandth of a gram. A few of the particles seen by Pioneer 10 were as large as 10 to 20 cm in diameter. Analysis of the Pioneer 10 data suggests that there are almost three times as many of these larger particles inside the asteroid belt as there are between the Earth and the belt. The data from Pioneer 11 confirm this finding.

Thus, the findings of the two Pioneer spacecraft indicate that the asteroid belt does not contain high-velocity projectiles which might penetrate spacecraft and damage them. Particles in the center of the belt which orbit the Sun at about 61,200 km (38,000 mi.) per hour would penetrate one centimeter thick aluminum even if the particle weighed only 0.001 gram. But most of the particles seen by Pioneer 10 and Pioneer 11 were smaller than this, and the total number of such particles was found to be far lower than had been predicted prior to the Pioneer mission. Though the belt contains quite large bodies as well as dust, dangerous concentrations of high-velocity dust particles that would be hazards to spacecraft do not seem to exist in the belt.

Just after Pioneer 11 emerged from the asteroid belt its trajectory was modified by command from Earth. On 19 April, 1974, thrusters on the spacecraft were commanded to add another 63.7 meters per sec (210.2 ft/sec) to the spacecraft's velocity thereby correcting the aiming point at Jupiter to 43,000 km (26,725 mi.) above the cloud tops. The main mission of Pioneer 11 at Jupiter was to penetrate deeper into the radiation belts. The inner radiation belt of the planet could easily destroy electronics of a spacecraft if the intensity of particles continued to increase beyond the maximum measured by Pioneer 10 at its closest approach to 2.86 Jovian radii; i.e., 132,252 km (82,000 mi.) above the cloud tops. So Pioneer 11 was directed to approach three times closer than Pioneer 10 and thereby obtain unique scientific observations of both Jupiter and its environment. The close approach also allowed the spacecraft to be accelerated by Jupiter to a velocity of 55 times that of the muzzle velocity of a high speed rifle bullet — to 173,000 km (108,000 mi.) per hour — so that it would be carried across the Solar System some 2.4 billion km (1.5 billion mi.) to Saturn.

Meanwhile, as Pioneer 11 cruised toward Jupiter, the interest in the giant planet sparked by the findings of Pioneer 10 was producing new discoveries by Earth-based observations.

Charles Kowal, a research assistant in astronomy at Caltech, developed a new technique to search for small objects near the giant planet. Using the Palomar Schmidt telescope's enormous light gathering power, a special screen to mask the glare of Jupiter, and photographic plates baked in nitrogen gas to increase sensitivity, Kowal discovered a thirteenth satellite of Jupiter in September 1974. (A fourteenth satellite was discovered a year later while Pioneer 11 was on its way to Saturn.) These satellites were too small to be seen by the imaging system of Pioneer.

The trajectory of the Pioneer 11 spacecraft had been selected to approach Jupiter from below the South Pole so that it would hurtle almost straight up through the intense radiation belt and thereby reduce the time of exposure to the radiation (Figure 5-17). B. J. O'Brien, Pioneer project manager at

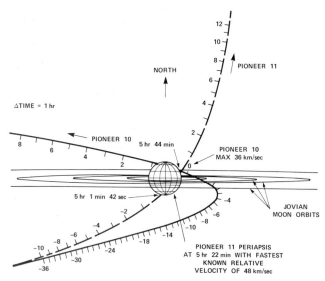

Figure 5-17. Pioneer 10 and 11 encounters with Jupiter, as viewed from Earth. The hour time marks show spacecraft locations relative to the periapsis target point.

TRW where the spacecraft were built, told the press that the total radiation dose Pioneer 11 would be expected to receive will be less than Pioneer 10's, "and we're betting that's what counts."

The problem is that the billions of electrons and protons that are trapped in Jupiter's magnetic field bombard the spacecraft. Some of these particles are traveling fast enough to dislodge electrons from atoms and even dislodge whole atoms in the spacecraft. When this happens to a critical part of the spacecraft's electronics spurious information can be generated or the electronics fail completely. Explained O'Brien: "Pioneer 10 passed along the magnetic equator, where most energetic particles appear to concentrate. The spacecraft took lots of hits over a long time. But Pioneer 11 will go in slow, slip through the area of maximum radiation fast, and come out in the clear pretty quickly. The radiation counts will probably soar at a pace that will scare us half to death just before closest approach, but the total dose Pioneer 11 receives won't be as great as Pioneer 10 took because the time will be much shorter."

"Pioneer 11 will be out of communication with Earth at the time of closest approach," continued O'Brien. "It will have gone behind Jupiter at 9:01 p.m., 21 minutes before closest approach. Its

onboard magnetic memory will be recording data for later transmission to Earth. Then we sit and wait .... and fidget. At 9:44 p.m., 22 minutes after closest approach, Pioneer 11 will come out from behind Jupiter. But we have another 40 minutes wait before we hear anything because of the signal's travel time from the distance of Jupiter to the Earth. So, at 10.24 p.m., if Pioneer is still working, we'll hear that we made it."

The close path by Jupiter would also provide a bonus in that it permitted images of the polar regions of the giant planet to be obtained by the spin-scan system, thereby providing views of Jupiter that can never be obtained from Earth observation. And unlike Pioneer 10, Pioneer 11 was directed to fly by Jupiter against the direction of the planet's rotation (Figure 5-18). After passing in front of Jupiter as the planet moves along its orbit round the Sun, the spacecraft then goes around the dark side of Jupiter and completes a circuit of the planet by crossing the spacecraft's own incoming trajectory and heading for Saturn.

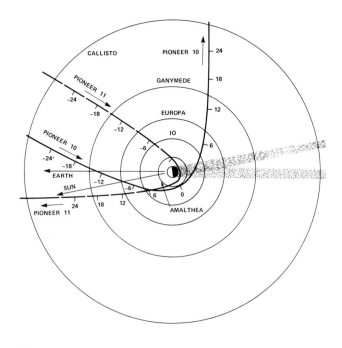

Figure 5-18. Pioneer 10 and 11 encounters with Jupiter as viewed from the celestial North Pole. Pioneer 10 swings around the giant in the counterclockwise direction, but Pioneer 11 attacks the planet in a clockwise course. Jupiter rotates counterclockwise in this view. The time in hours before and after closest approach is given by the numbers alongside each trajectory.

84

Views of Jupiter as seen from the spacecraft are shown in Figure 5-19. These PICS images returned from the spacecraft were displayed live to many thousands of interested people over cable TV in the San Francisco Bay area. During the encounter, several of the public halls to which the TV images and a running commentary by astronaut Colonel A. Worden were relayed were jammed to capacity for many hours.

Before closest approach to Jupiter, the spacecraft's view of the planet showed the terminator boundary between day and night on the planet — near the left hand edge of the disc. After closest approach the terminator was near the upper right-hand edge of the disc. The south polar regions were seen prior to closest approach and the north polar regions afterwards.

As with Pioneer 10 there were five phases to the encounter. The first occupied about three weeks starting 3 November 1974, when the spacecraft passed from interplanetary space into the Jovian system, moving from about 24 million to 10 million km (15 million to 6 million mi.) from the planet.

Phase two covered entry of Pioneer 11 into the inner system, following penetration of the bow shock wave in the solar wind created by the interaction of Jupiter's magnetic field with that wind. This occurred on 25 November 1974 at 10:00 p.m. PST. Almost a day later — 9:00 p.m. PST on 26 November — the spacecraft entered the magnetosphere where the magnetic field of Jupiter prevents the wind from approaching closer to the surface of the planet. Pioneer 11 was now 7 million km (4.3 million mi.) from Jupiter. But at 10:20 a.m. PST on 27 November at a distance of 6.6 million km (4.1 million mi.), Pioneer 11 popped out of the magnetosphere for five and a half hours before crossing the bow shock again and returning into the magnetosphere at 6.44 million km (4.0 million mi.) from Jupiter. These repeated bow shock crossings, first experienced by Pioneer 10, confirmed the model of the Jovian magnetosphere that likens it to an unstable soft balloon that is buffeted by the solar wind and often squeezed in towards Jupiter on the side facing the Sun.

The third phase of the encounter was when Pioneer 11 continued flying through the outer magnetosphere from about 4.8 to 3.2 million km (3 to 2 million mi.) from the planet.

Phase four, the period around closest approach, covering the day and a half before and after periapsis, was where the spacecraft made most of its measurements and obtained the better spin-scan images of Jupiter and the large satellites.

During stage five Pioneer 11 left Jupiter behind and repeated many of the earlier experiments but in reverse sequence.

November 7, Pioneer 11 crossed the orbit of Hades, outermost satellite of Jupiter. In the next few days the spacecraft successively crossed the orbits of Pan and Andrastea. By 21 November, Pioneer had crossed the orbit of Hera at just over 11.25 million km (7 million mi.) from Jupiter; then the orbits of Demeter and Hestia. But the Jovian system is so large that despite Pioneer 11's enormous speed it was not until 1 December, the day before closest approach, that the spacecraft began to cross the orbits of the large Galilean satellites. There were no really close approaches to these satellites. Pioneer 11 came within 786,000 km (488,700 mi.) of Callisto, within 692,200 km (430,200 mi.) of Ganymede, and within 265,500 km (195,000 mi.) of Io. Finally Pioneer passed within 587,000 km (365,000 mi.) of Europa, and within 127,000 km (79,000 mi.) of the innermost satellite, Amalthea.

Spin scan images were obtained of several of these satellites (see Chapter 9).

By this time TV screens at NASA's Ames Research Center were displaying good-sized images of Jupiter showing an orange and grey-white striped sphere with detailed cloud features and a prominent Great Red Spot (see Figure 5-19).

The excellent image of the Great Red Spot, shown in Chapter 9, was only obtained as a result of quick revision to the command sequences for the spacecraft. Pioneer 11 was flying by Jupiter at high speed in the opposite direction to the rotation

Figure 5-19. This series of PICS images shows views of Jupiter as
viewed from Pioneer 11 as it approached the planet from the
south, flew by, and then rose high above the north polar region.

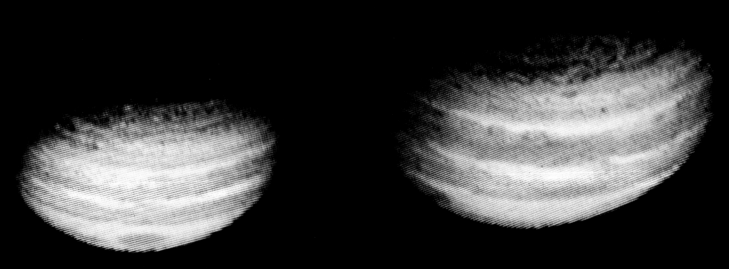

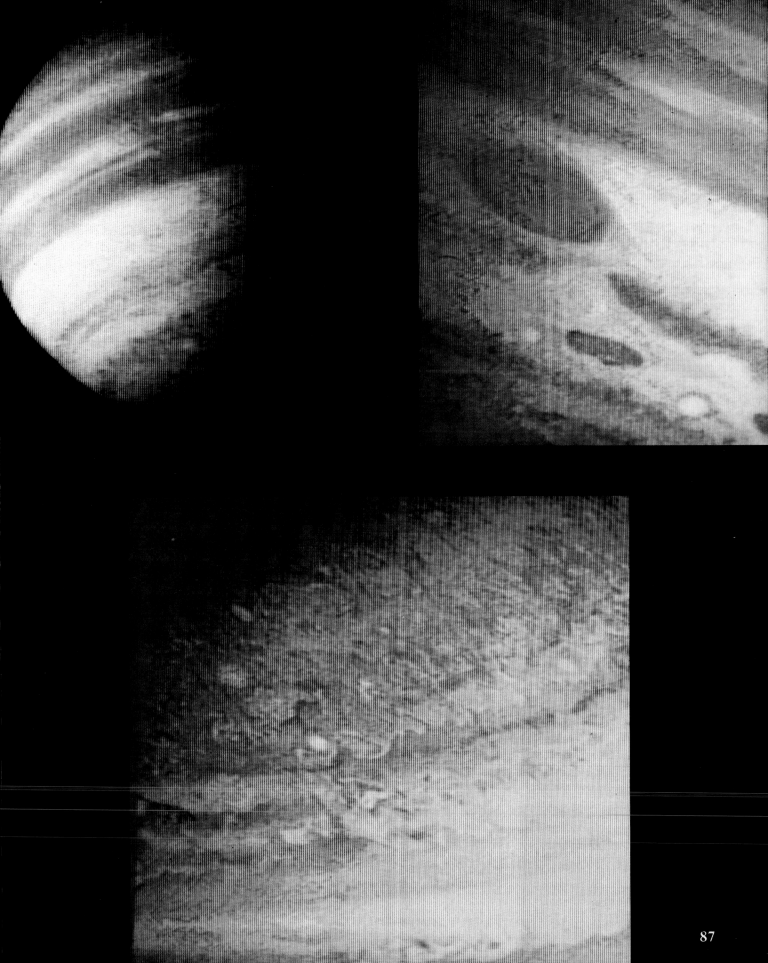

of Jupiter on its axis. The combination of these two rapid motions made it mandatory for the timing of a close-in image of the spot to be extremely precise.

Months before the encounter Lyn Doose of University of Arizona, working with the imaging photopolarimeter team, contacted ground-based observatories to determine the spot's position and drift rate in order to estimate where it would be precisely at the time of Pioneer 11's flyby. When a final position had been established, a series of computer drawings was prepared, simulating how the planet would appear to the spacecraft at one-hour intervals during the close encounter. From these drawings the best observing opportunity was selected and reserved for imaging of the Red Spot; other activity of the imaging photopolarimeter was worked around the timing for the Red Spot image.

Just before encounter Doose explained: "A somewhat different approach from that used on Pioneer 10 would be employed. The Red Spot would be scanned nearer to the center of the planet's illuminated hemisphere so that it would not be foreshortened and would be well away from the terminator and evenly illuminated."

"The commands to the imaging photopolarimeter were written, rewritten, checked and rechecked," continued Doose. "Only ten days before the flyby we discovered an error. The time for obtaining the best image of the spot as derived from the computer-generated drawings was referenced to when the telescope should execute the commands, but they had been interpreted as being when the commands should be transmitted."

"The rotation of Jupiter, coupled with the motion of the spacecraft would have put the Red Spot outside the field of view of the image."

For two days the imaging command sequence for the several hours before closest approach was revised. New commands were written and command files were prepared for transmission to the spacecraft in the tight command sequence. With these last minute changes the Red Spot sequence worked perfectly and a unique image of the Great Red Spot was obtained (see Figure 9-11).

As well as presenting higher latitudes to the spin-scan imaging system, the flyby trajectory chosen allowed the magnetic field and radiation environment to be explored to higher latitudes of the magnetosphere. Also, while Pioneer 10 maintained an almost constant view relative to Jupiter for several hours during closest approach because its direction of travel was the same as the direction of rotation of Jupiter, Pioneer 11 traveled oppositely to Jupiter's rotation and traversed a full circle of longitude of the planet during its close observations in the 4 hours around periapsis.

Approximately 1300 commands were transmitted to Pioneer 11 on each of two days at closest approach. Many of these commands were intended to make sure that the equipment carried by the spacecraft would continue to operate in a correct configuration in spite of the effects of the radiation environment. Thus the spacecraft was repeatedly commanded to the correct data format, to the correct data bit rate, to keep the transmitter switched on, and to keep the scientific experiments operating. Also the spin-scan imaging photometer, which lost several important images during Pioneer 10 encounter because of false commands generated by radiation, was periodically reset (indexed) to a basic position from which it was directed to the correct aspect angle for planetary imaging. This command technique had proved invaluable during the encounter of Pioneer 10 and was now expanded in scope for the more rigorous encounter of Pioneer 11.

The more serious problem than the radiation environment of Jupiter was a threatened strike of diesel operators in Australia which endangered the mission in the last few hours before close encounter. The strikers permitted technical personnel to operate the ground station for the encounter. Had this not been permitted the mission would have lost 6 to 8 hours of scientific data each day. Flight operations could not be certain that the Deep Space Network station at Canberra would, indeed, be available for the encounter — the strike situation looked so bad. In the less than 30 minutes available they reprogrammed the encounter sequence to enable the Goldstone Deep Space Station to maintain communications with the spacecraft for a longer period than normally, almost until the spacecraft set at Goldstone. This also required the bit rate to be dropped from 2048 to 1024 bits per second. So the mission was seriously endangered by social problems on Earth more so than the harsh environment half a billion miles from Earth.

The spacecraft went behind Jupiter at 9:02 p.m. PST on 2 December. The telemetered signals continued until 9:42 p.m. PST because of the time delay in transmission over the millions of miles to Earth. Now everyone waited anxiously. It was during this occultation that the spacecraft would hurtle through its closest approach to Jupiter, skimming 43,000 km (26,725 mi.) above the cloud tops as it passed through the greatest intensity of the radiation belts. Would it survive?

The scheduled emergence from behind Jupiter was 9:44 p.m. PST, 22 minutes after closest approach. But the signals, if they were still coming from the spacecraft would not arrive at Earth until 10:24 p.m. PST.

Everyone waited.

Eleven seconds after 10:24:05 p.m. PST, the Deep Space Network station at Canberra, Australia, picked up the signal and relayed it to the Pioneer Mission Control at Ames Research Center. Engineers, scientists, and newsmen covering the event at Ames Research Center cheered. Ten seconds later the big antenna at Goldstone in the Mojave Desert of California picked up the whisper-faint signals from the distant spacecraft. All was well. Pioneer 11 had survived its encounter with the giant of the Solar System.

Anomalies occurred during flyby in the plasma analyzer, the infrared radiometer, the meteoroid detector and the spin-scan imaging photopolarimeter. Also there was a small decrease in output current of the spacecraft power system; but this was less than that experienced by Pioneer 10 and caused no difficulties.

The most serious problem was spurious commands that caused the infrared radiometer to miss observing the northern hemisphere of Jupiter. As soon as the signals reached Earth and the problem was detected the project science chief and the science advisor immediately prepared a 108-command sequence to correct the infrared radiometer register settings thereby saving 50 percent of the planned observations from the northern hemisphere.

In the next few hours scientists were able to analyze the details of the radiation belts and fantastic spin-scan images were returned to Earth of the northern hemisphere of Jupiter. Predictions of the high energy electron intensity during the close passage proved to be correct, but, surprisingly, the actual proton flux measured was about ten times less than that predicted in advance of the flyby and based on extrapolations from the Pioneer 10 data. Pioneer 11 showed that near the planet the radiation belt is intense but occupies a smaller volume than expected. Though Pioneer 10 and 11 found shells of dangerous, extremely-high-energy protons near Jupiter's magnetic equator, the shells were only at low latitudes and posed a relatively minor hazard to spacecraft flying through them at highly inclined trajectories. Also, the intensity of high energy electrons turned out to be only slightly higher than that found by Pioneer 10 even though Pioneer 11 went three times closer to the planet. But Pioneer also found that there is a flux at higher latitudes that is greater than expected from the Pioneer 10 results.

Again the picture emerged of an enormous spinning magnetic field buffeted by the solar wind and stirred by Amalthea and the Galilean satellites.

During this encounter, Pioneer 11 determined very accurately the mass of Callisto as 1.5 lunar masses. Also the close approach provided more accurate determinations of the gravitational field of Jupiter itself.

In making the first observations of Jupiter's immense polar regions (Figure 5-20) Pioneer 11 found that the planet's cloud tops are substantially lower at the poles than at the equator, and are covered by a thicker but transparent atmosphere. Though there is much less evidence of rapid atmospheric circulation at the poles than at the equator,

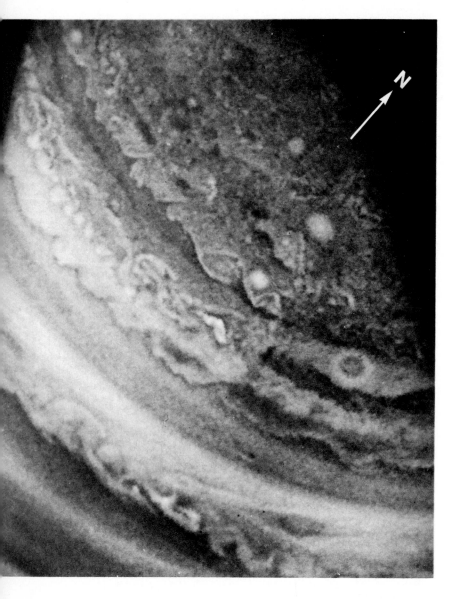

Figure 5-20. Pioneer 11 obtained the first photographs of Jupiter's polar regions.

the polar areas unexpectedly showed many small convective cells, dwarfing similar Earth thunderstorms. Blue sky was also visible at the poles and is attributed to the same cause as Earth's blue skies — multiple molecule scattering of light by gases of the transparent atmosphere at Jupiter's poles.

Many more flow features were also revealed in the clouds around the Great Red Spot than were seen a year previously by Pioneer 10. And within the spot new details were revealed that suggested convection and circulation patterns. The center of the spot appeared brighter than its edges.

Immediately after the encounter with Jupiter, Pioneer 11 was renamed Pioneer Saturn as it headed to an exploration of the next outer planet of our Solar System. Several weeks after the encounter, problems arose in the spacecraft with spurious commands which could not be attributed to radiation. These problems continued for several months as Pioneer 11 headed toward Saturn. Analysis of special test results indicated that the asteroid-meteoroid detector had been damaged by radiation during the encounter and was now the source of the signals responsible for the spurious commands. The instrument was turned off and the spurious commands ended. But in the series of tests to isolate the cause of the spurious commands by turning off each piece of equipment in turn, the plasma analyzer was switched off. When commanded on again, the power for the instrument turned on but the instrument did not produce data. This instrument, important for the flyby of Saturn is being subjected to special command sequences to try to reestablish data output for the encounter with the ringed planet.

The unique ringed planet Saturn (Figure 5-21) has so low a density it would float in an ocean big enough to contain it. It is a large planet, 120,800 km (75,000 mi.) in diameter, which revolves around our Sun in 29.46 years at a mean distance of 1,426,000,000 km (886,000,000 mi.). Like Jupiter it rotates very rapidly on its axis — in 10 hours and 14 minutes — and is flattened considerably at the poles and bulged at the equator by this rapid spin.

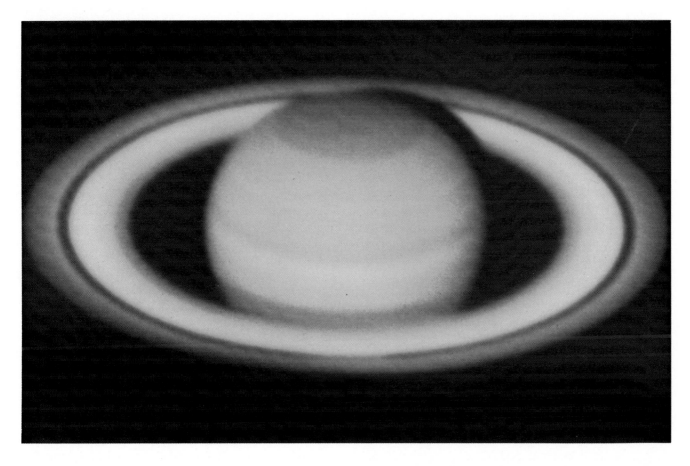

Figure 5-21. The planet Saturn with its unique ring system is the second target for Pioneer 11 after its encounter with giant Jupiter. Pioneer 11 was renamed Pioneer-Saturn.

(Photo. Catalina Observatory)

Its 278,600 km (174,200 mi.) diameter ring system is unique among planets of the Solar System.

The objectives of Pioneer 11 at the ringed planet are very similar to the science objectives at Jupiter:

★ Map the magnetic field of Saturn and determine its intensity, direction, and structure. Although such a field has not been detected from Earth, several experts in planetary magnetism believe that Saturn does have a magnetic field. Saturn is also believed to have a massive core, possibly extending to 30 percent of its radius. Such a core is inferred from the motions of natural satellites and would support the probability of Saturn having a magnetic field.

★ Determine how many electrons and protons of various energies are distributed along the trajectory of the spacecraft through the Saturn system.

★ Map the interaction of the Saturn system with the solar wind.

★ Measure the temperature of Saturn's atmosphere and that of Titan, the large satellite of Saturn.

★ Determine the structure of the upper atmosphere of Saturn where molecules are expected to be electrically charged and form an ionosphere.

★ Map the thermal structure of Saturn's atmosphere by infrared observations coupled with radio occultation data.

★ Obtain spin-scan images of Saturn in two colors during the encounter sequence, and close-up images of special planetary features, including the ring system, and make polarimetry measurements of the planet, the rings, and some of the satellites.

★ Probe the ring system and the atmosphere of Saturn with S-band radio waves at occultation.

★ Determine more precisely the masses of Saturn and its larger satellites by accurate observations of the effects of their gravitational fields on the motion of the spacecraft.

★ Obtain information to calculate with greater accuracy the orbits and ephemerides of Saturn and its larger satellites.

★ As a precursor to the Mariner Jupiter/Saturn mission, verify the environment of the ring plane to find out where it may be safely crossed by the Mariner spacecraft without serious damage.

Two target locations have been tentatively suggested for the flyby of Saturn; an outside target results in penetrating the ring plane just outside the outer visible (A) ring with a closest approach to Saturn of 1.4 planetary radii and an escape from the system past Titan. An inside target results in penetration within the visible rings — penetrating at 1.15 radii of Saturn and approaching to 1.06 radii — but directly through the D-ring which was discovered photographically only recently. The inside passage may damage the spacecraft so that its subsequent close passage by Titan would not provide any data on that intriguing satellite. On the other hand, close passage outside the A ring is not

certain to be safer.

Either of these two trajectories can be chosen as late as 1977 when the spacecraft will be aligned in space so that it can be most accurately maneuvered to the selected course. During this maneuver the time of arrival at Saturn would be changed to insure dual coverage by stations of the Deep Space Network at the hour of closest approach to Saturn.

The celestial mechanics of the Pioneer Saturn encounter might best be exploited through the flyby that carries Pioneer inside the innermost visible ring and about 9000 km (5000 mi.) above the cloud tops of the planet (Figure 5-22). Such a close approach to the planet would not only define most accurately Saturn's gravitational field, but also provide data which, when combined with corresponding observations from a Mariner Jupiter/Saturn flyby in 1981, would allow a good estimate of the mass of the ring system to be made.

The close approach also provides information about the internal structure and shape of Saturn. Even if the spacecraft is damaged or put out of action by its passage through the ring plane, valuable gravitational data would still be obtained prior to penetration of the ring plane.

If the spacecraft arrives at Saturn during the few hours from late evening on 1 September 1979 to early morning on 2 September, a close approach can also permit the spacecraft to leave the planet in a direction that would carry it close to Titan about 26 hours after its periapsis with Saturn.

The large satellite Titan is known to have an atmosphere. The diameter of Titan is about 4800 km (3000 mi.) and this satellite is regarded as a prime candidate among bodies of our Solar System that might support life. The constituents of its atmosphere are believed to be of the type that supported primitive life forms on Earth before the terrestrial atmosphere became oxygen enriched. Titan orbits Saturn in just under 16 days at a mean distance of 1,222,000 km (759,300 mi.).

If Pioneer Saturn does survive its passage through the plane of Saturn's ring system and any radiation environment of Saturn, its subsequent

PIONEER SPACECRAFT
TRAJECTORY

Figure 5-22. One of several options to fly by Saturn would carry
the Pioneer spacecraft behind the rings as well as the planet and
provide occultations to probe the rings and the planetary atmosphere with the radio signals from the spacecraft to Earth. The
marks on the trajectory signify periods of one hour. The trajectory after encounter carries the spacecraft alongside Titan for an
inspection of that large satellite.

93

close approach to Titan, will measure the satellite's mass more accurately. It will also obtain spin-scan images of the surface of the satellite which might show large surface markings, measure the temperature of the surface, and improve the ephemeris to aid future missions. However, much depends on the choice of the path for Pioneer past Saturn.

A complication in selecting the time of arrival of Pioneer 11 at Saturn is the motion of the Earth around the Sun. As Saturn moves relative to the Earth to pass behind the Sun as seen from Earth, radio noise from the Sun will interfere with the faint radio signals from the spacecraft. So arrival at Saturn has to be timed in advance of Saturn moving into superior conjunction which takes place 11 September 1979. The Sun-Earth-spacecraft angle is closing at about 1 degree per day around the time of the encounter, so moving the encounter forward in time provides an opportunity to have a subsequent encounter with Titan and still receive radio signals back from the spacecraft. Unfortunately there may be about 1 week of observations of the magnetosphere lost on the outward leg of the flight beyond Saturn because the spacecraft will pass behind the Sun as viewed from Earth and its signals will be lost in solar noise.

At the distance of Saturn it will also be necessary to accept a reduced bit rate for data transmission; only 256 bits per second compared with 1024 from Jupiter. This lower bit rate will primarily affect the data from imaging and will reduce the image scans to smaller sectors of about one half to one quarter those possible at Jupiter.

After its encounter with Saturn, Pioneer 11 will move in almost the plane of the ecliptic in a flight direction opposite to that of Pioneer 10. The second Pioneer will thus be heading out of the Solar System in the same direction approximately as that in which the Solar System is moving through the Galaxy. The small spacecraft is expected to reach its limits of communication with Earth at about 20 Earth-Sun distances in 1986. Then it and its sister spacecraft will continue out towards the beckoning stars, mankind's first emissaries into interstellar space.

6
Results at the New Frontiers

ON ITS WAY to the historic encounter with Jupiter, Pioneer 10 completed a number of scientific experiments in the unexplored space beyond the orbit of Mars. After encounter, these experiments continued and are expected to do so for many years. They were supplemented by information from Pioneer 11, which also proceeded beyond Jupiter to explore Saturn and then the outer Solar System. By contrast with exploration of the inner Solar System, these new scientific frontiers are probed more slowly because of the vast distances involved. It may be decades before all the scientific information is analyzed and evaluated.

But already a broadening understanding emerges of the Solar System beyond Mars from the data gathered by these pioneering spacecraft. The new information describes the interplanetary medium beyond the orbit of Mars, the asteroid belt, and the environment of the Jovian system, together with more accurate physical details of Jupiter itself.

The Interplanetary Medium Beyond the Orbit of Mars

Theoretically the solar wind, blowing through the interplanetary medium, might be expected to expand radially from the Sun in a symmetrical fashion so as to expand and cool adiabatically; i.e., it does not exchange heat with its surroundings. In such a theoretical model, the temperature of the solar wind would decrease with distance according to a four-thirds power law. At the distance of the Earth from the Sun, experiments showed that this law is not quite valid — the solar wind behaves somewhat differently — and it seems that nonuniformities in the solar wind arise from hot spots in the solar corona. Since the temperature of the solar corona determines the speed of the solar wind, such hot spots would be expected to give rise to solar wind streams of different speeds. Moreover, because the Sun rotates on its axis, a fast moving stream of the solar wind can catch up with a slow moving stream that starts out earlier from a cooler part of the corona.

When a fast stream catches up with a slow moving stream, it tries to penetrate it but is prevented from doing so by magnetic fields carried by the streams. These fields are carried along because the energy density of the solar wind is about 100 times the energy density of the interplanetary field.

The solar wind streams act somewhat like billiard balls, colliding and rebounding. There are steep magnetic gradients between the streams at the times of collision. It is the magnetic interface that becomes a scattering region for cosmic rays

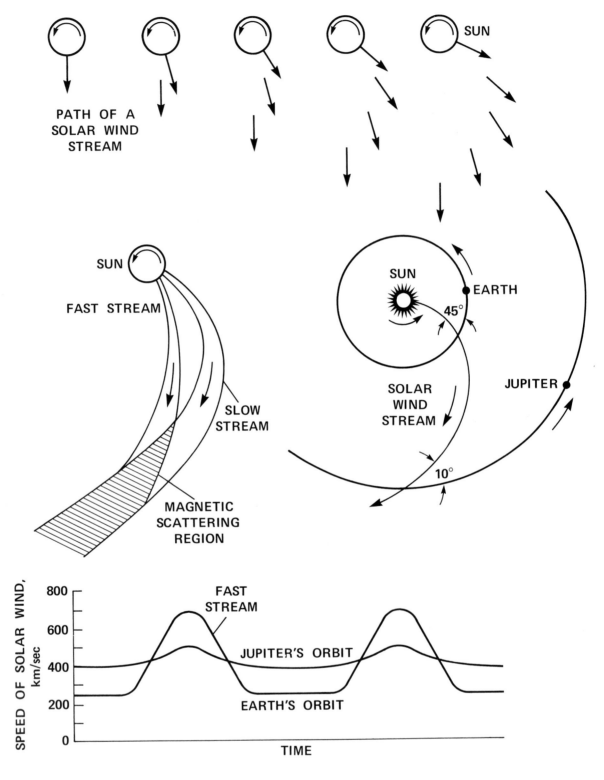

Figure 6-1. Fast streams of solar wind catch up with slow streams and produce scattering regions that prevent low energy cosmic rays from penetrating into the Solar System. The average velocity of the solar wind changes imperceptibly to the orbit of Jupiter but, as shown in the lower diagram, the range of fluctuations is remarkably diminished at this distance. Pioneer 10 and 11 might reach the boundary where this scattering effect ends and galactic cosmic rays would be expected to increase in intensity. To eight times Earth's distance from the Sun there is no sign of approaching such a boundary.

coming into the Solar System from the Galaxy, not the solar wind itself (Figure 6-1).

Because of these scattering centers, no low energy cosmic rays are able to penetrate into the inner Solar System. The question is: how far into the Solar System do the low energy galactic cosmic rays penetrate?

It is predicted from the Pioneer observations that the scattering regions will not damp down until perhaps 20 to 30 times Earth's distance from the Sun. This distance will be reached by the Pioneer spacecraft. Pioneer 11 is moving in the same direction as the Solar System is traveling through the Galaxy in the direction of a hypothetical bow shock of the heliosphere and the interstellar medium, and Pioneer 10 is traveling in the opposite direction. The heliopause, or boundary of the heliosphere, is expected to be closer to the Sun along the trajectory of Pioneer 11.

The question is: will the spacecraft be able to return information from so far away? The survival of Pioneer to the vast distances beyond Jupiter is very important in checking on the changes to the solar wind in the outer Solar System. And, if all goes well, both Pioneers should do this, though Pioneer 11 may not survive its encounter with Saturn, particularly if it passes through the inner ring plane. Even as the RTG power supply output begins to fall due to an expected decreased output from the power-converting thermopiles, experiments can be cycled — shut off and then later brought on again — to conserve power and store this power in the battery for short periods of data transmission to the limits of communications distance — possibly to 20 times Earth's distance from the Sun, i.e., some two billion miles.

The very low intrinsic magnetic field of the Pioneer spacecraft makes it possible to investigate the extremely weak interplanetary magnetic field far out into the Solar System. Additionally, because the flight of Pioneer 10 is at a time of minimum solar activity in the 11-year solar cycle, the effects of the Sun on cosmic rays are at a minimum too. Thus, these particles from the Galaxy, possibly representing material from a dense con-

centration of stars at the center of the Galaxy, may be penetrating far enough into the Solar System for the Pioneers to detect them. To eight times Earth's distance from the Sun Pioneer 10 has shown that contrary to some theories there is no increase in the intensity of galactic cosmic rays consisting of particles with energies above 80 MeV. Traditional cosmic ray theory has assumed that as the solar wind is diffused at increasing distances from the Sun, the intensity of galactic cosmic rays would increase. The Pioneer measurements are five times less than the intensities expected by traditional cosmic ray modulation theory.

One speculation gaining credence today is that a proportion of these lower energy 'cosmic rays' is not in fact of galactic origin but instead consists of ions of the solar wind accelerated to higher energies within the magnetospheres of planets of the Solar System. Moreover, the results point toward an increased possibility that the heliosphere extends much farther from the Sun than once thought — even as far as 100 times Earth's distance from the Sun, i.e., far beyond the orbit of Pluto.

Pioneer 11 will follow Pioneer 10 into the outer Solar System. If the second spacecraft survives its encounter with Saturn and its rings it, too, will investigate the heliosphere and the magnetic fields in the outer Solar System. These two Pioneers have advantages over the Mariner Jupiter/Saturn spacecraft in that they are magnetically very clean and are exploring the Solar System at a time when, because solar activity is minimal, the heliopause might be expected to be closer to the Sun.

The two Pioneer spacecraft may clear up much of the present speculation about the origin of cosmic rays and the flux of light and of particles from stars in general (Figure 6-2). One of the big questions facing astronomers is whether or not stars give off as much energy in particles as they do in light. Looking from Earth at the entire sky, they find that the light energy received from stars is about equal to the energy of incoming cosmic rays. Yet, the output of the Sun is very different: it pours out much more energy in the form of light than as particles. So it could be that the high cosmic ray flux from the Galaxy is some purely local effect, such as from the violent explosion of a star or a group of stars in our part of the Galaxy, or the charged particle residue from the death of very old stars formed billions of years before our own Sun, and trapped within the magnetic confines of our Galaxy, or even generated locally in planetary magnetospheres.

Figure 6-2. A big unanswered question is whether cosmic rays come from the stars in general (a) or from exploding stars (b) in the neighborhood of the Solar System. (*Photo: Hale Observatories*)

Pioneer experiments showed that as far out as 565 million km (350 million mi.) from the Sun, solar magnetic field strength, solar wind density, and numbers of solar high energy particles, all declined roughly as the square of distance from the Sun, as was expected. But surprisingly, as mentioned earlier, the galactic cosmic ray intensity did not increase. As it moves outward, the solar wind stream becomes less variable while its gases cool much less rapidly; the high speed streams are converted into random thermal motions of particles (see lower diagram on Figure 6-1).

The experimenters found out, too, that the uncharged hydrogen atoms of an interstellar wind — the gas between the stars — stream into the Solar System along the plane of the Earth's orbit. Pioneer also found helium atoms in space for the first time. Experimenters believe that these, too, are from interstellar space.

Pioneer 10 produced new information about the Zodiacal Light, the faint band of light along the Zodiac, believed to be an effect of sunlight reflected from particles in interplanetary space. The slight enhancement of the glow exactly opposite to the Sun in the sky — the Gegenschein — could be caused by distant particles illuminated like miniature full moons opposite the Sun, or by a stream of particles extending as a comet's tail from Earth.

The imaging photopolarimeter was turned on March 10, 1972, seven days after Pioneer 10 was launched. During the first few weeks of the mission, when the Sun angle was about 26 degrees from the spacecraft's spin axis, only that part of the sky more than 60 degrees from the Sun line could be inspected by the imaging photopolarimeter. So observations concentrated on the Gegenschein. It quickly became apparent that the Gegenschein could not be associated with Earth because, although the spacecraft had not moved much farther from the Sun, it had moved ahead along the orbit of the Earth. While the direction of the Gegenschein was directly away from the Sun as seen from the spacecraft, this direction was by this time different from the direction of the Gegenschein from Earth (Figure 6-3). So the anti-solar glow was confirmed as being associated with the light reflected from particles spread around the Solar System, not from particles associated with the Earth itself. Experimenters later measured the faint glow of the Gegenschein to near the orbit of Mars, again confirming its interplanetary nature.

As Pioneer 10 moved away from the Sun, the brightness of the Gegenschein also decreased, thereby showing that it results from particles in the inner Solar System. There was, however, a decrease in the rate at which the brightness faded within the asteroid belt, which indicates that the particles responsible for the counterglow increase somewhat within the belt. But beyond the belt there is virtually no Gegenschein.

As Pioneer moved out from Earth, it became possible to start mapping the whole of the sky to look at the Zodiacal Light. Scientists found that the Zodiacal Light also decreases in brightness as the square of the distance from the Sun. The rate

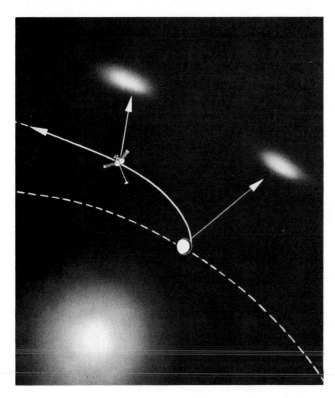

Figure 6-3. The Gegenschein cannot be associated with Earth because seen from Pioneer and seen from Earth it is in different directions in space.

of decrease slowed within the asteroid belt, indicating that particles responsible for the Zodiacal Light, although concentrated in the inner Solar System, also increase somewhat within the asteroid belt itself. But beyond three and a half times Earth's distance from the Sun, the Zodiacal Light is negligible, and experimenters were able to record the integrated starlight from the Galaxy free of the Zodiacal Light for the first time. Since the Zodiacal Light's brightness, at 2.41 times Earth's distance from the Sun, is less than one tenth that at Earth's orbit, experimenters conclude that the asteroid belt beyond this distance does not contribute significantly to the Zodiacal Light as seen from Earth. Zodiacal Light brightness fades almost completely at a distance of 3.3 times Earth's distance from the Sun. This is where particles would have to circle the Sun in orbits having a period of half that of Jupiter. Jupiter's gravity appears to sweep the Solar System clear of such particles beyond this resonance orbit. Thus, there is virtually no Zodiacal Light nor Gegenschein beyond the asteroid belt.

Meteoroids and the Asteroid Belt

Pioneer 10 provided some surprises even before reaching the orbit of Mars. At one time, it was speculated that because Soviet and U.S. spacecraft encountered trouble on their way to Mars at about 175 million km (110 million mi.) from the Sun, a concentration of asteroids occurred inside the orbit of Mars, or a band of dust inside the orbit of Mars presented a hazard to spacecraft. Pioneer 10 showed the speculation to be unfounded and provided data to suggest that Mars might even be sweeping its orbit clean of particles.

The 280 million km (175 million mi.) wide asteroid belt did not prove to be as hazardous as some speculation had suggested prior to Pioneer 10's epic voyage. Astronomers, who had observed the large number of minor planets in the asteroid belt, had postulated that the small bodies might be colliding with each other. As a consequence over the billions of years since the formation of the Solar System, these collisions might have populated the zone of the asteroids with innumerable particles, ranging in size from the major asteroids to grains of dust. Such particles in myriads could present a serious hazard to spacecraft.

By June of 1972, just before the spacecraft entered the asteroid belt, Pioneer 10's detector cells had recorded 41 puncturing impacts. These occurred at a fairly steady rate from launch in March of that year. By October, when Pioneer was half way through the belt, the counting rate remained much the same and another 42 impacts had been recorded. This rate continued relatively unchanged all the way through the belt.

But, by the middle of February 1973, Pioneer 10 had cleared the asteroid belt safely. There was no indication of myriad tiny bodies ready to pepper any spacecraft in these regions of space. Thus, from a hazardous particle point of view, there appeared to be no asteroid belt. Fine particles seem to be fairly evenly distributed between the planets. These results confirm the Zodiacal Light and Gegenschein observations, and imply that the asteroid belt is not a serious hazard to spacecraft traversing it.

Pioneer 11 confirmed these results as it also penetrated the asteroid belt safely.

Also, very small particles of interplanetary dust seem to be swept by Mars and Earth to produce a gap from 1.14 to 1.34 times Earth's distance from the Sun, while they appear to be concentrated in the vicinity of Jupiter by Jupiter's gravity. This concentration at Jupiter was detected by Pioneer 10 undergoing 300 times more impacts of the tiny dust particles as it had in any region of interplanetary space since leaving Earth. Such a concentration around Jupiter is not a hazard to spacecraft flying by the planet, but may be a hazard to orbiting spacecraft.

Pioneer 10 detected an increase in the number of meteoroid-sized particles hitting its detectors as it flew by Jupiter, suggesting a one hundred-fold increase in dust density compared with that in interplanetary space. The Pioneer 11 detector —

because its design was less sensitive to small particles — detected fewer particles during its flyby. But the number of particles detected in the steeply inclined and retrograde trajectory of Pioneer 11 appears to be consistent with the gravitational collection of particles from interplanetary space by the mass of Jupiter rather than a dust zone surrounding Jupiter analogous to the rings of Saturn.

The Jovian System

The paths of the two Pioneer spacecraft through the Jovian system, observed by tracking them from Earth, revealed that the system — Jupiter plus the satellites — is heavier than previously calculated by about twice the mass of Earth's Moon. Jupiter, itself, is about one Moon mass heavier than previously calculated — namely 317.8 Earth masses.

The close approach (to 1.62 Jupiter radii from the center of the planet) by Pioneer 11 provided additional details of the gravitational field of the giant planet and confirmed the Pioneer 10 results.

Analysis of the gravity field results from the Pioneer 11 flyby shows that Jupiter is a very symmetrical planet, almost as though it had been turned on a lathe and with no gravitational anomalies like those of the terrestrial planets. This situation is best modeled by a planet that is almost entirely liquid.

A new measurement of the diameter of Jupiter and of the planet's polar flattening was made. Jupiter is slightly more flattened than derived from the best visual observations from Earth. The diameter of the planet was measured at a pressure of 800 millibars near to the cloud tops. Its polar diameter is 135,516 km (82,967 mi.) compared with an equatorial diameter of 142,796 km (88,734 mi.). These new values were confirmed by the timing of the occultation of the spacecraft by Jupiter. Thus, Jupiter is ten times as flattened as is Earth, probably because of its fluid state and its high speed of rotation. The average density of Jupiter, calculated from its mass and its volume, is confirmed at one and one third that of water.

100

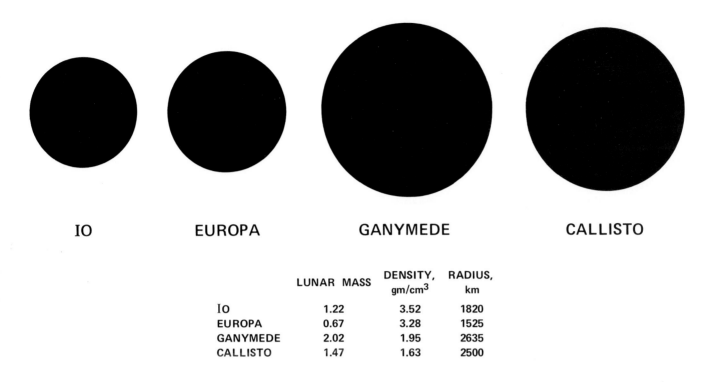

	LUNAR MASS	DENSITY, gm/cm^3	RADIUS, km
Io	1.22	3.52	1820
EUROPA	0.67	3.28	1525
GANYMEDE	2.02	1.95	2635
CALLISTO	1.47	1.63	2500

Figure 6-4. Pioneer 10 provided specific information on the physical characteristics of the Jovian satellites.

The Pioneers provided new information about the physical characteristics of the large Jovian satellites (Figure 6-4). In terms of the mass of Earth's Moon (1/81 of Earth's mass), the masses of the satellites in order of distance from Jupiter are determined as: Io, 1.22; Europa, 0.67; Ganymede, 2.02; and Callisto, 1.44 lunar masses. This measurement of Io's mass is 23 percent greater than that calculated before the Pioneer odyssey. The density of the satellites decreases with increasing distance from Jupiter and was refined as the result of Pioneer 11 observations — Io's density is 3.52 times that of water; Europa's, 3.28; Ganymede's, 1.95; and Callisto's, 1.63. The two inner satellites thus seem to be rocky bodies — Io's density is, indeed, greater than that of Earth's Moon — while the outer satellites could consist largely of water ice to account for their low density. The four satellites each have an average daylight surface temperature of about −145° C (−230° F).

It would seem that these satellites formed in such a way that lighter elements were depleted close to Jupiter or that water did not condense on Io and Europa because of their higher temperature near to Jupiter either during the condensation from the original nebula or as a result of subsequent heating of Jupiter.

Pioneer 10 was occulted by Io and, thus, was able to probe into the satellite's atmosphere. While a spurious command prevented a spin-scan image of Io, images were obtained of Europa and Ganymede. The Ganymede picture resolves features to 400 km (240 mi.) and shows a south polar mare and a central mare, each about 800 km (480 mi.) in diameter, and a bright north polar region (Figure 6-5). These isolated dark areas may, however, be areas where frost is not being formed as fast (by upwelling from the liquid watery interior) as evaporation takes place from a surface that is essentially without an atmosphere.

Figure 6-5. Ganymede appears more like Mars than the Moon or Mercury in this close-in spin-scan image from Pioneer 10. Earlier eclipse observations from Earth suggested that Ganymede has a surface of high porosity, the upper half-inch of which might be composed of loose, fine-grained rock.

Figure 6-6. Europa was too far away for Pioneer to obtain a detailed image. (See also Chapter 9.)

Probed by radar from Earth, Ganymede appears to have a surface rougher than Mercury, Mars or the Moon. This Jovian satellite may have a surface consisting of rocky or metallic material embedded in ice. While weathered smooth on the surface, the blocks of material within the ice would present a rough surface to the radar probing since the ice is relatively transparent to radar of the wavelengths used.

A less detailed spin-scan image of Europa by Pioneer 10 shows a somewhat similar appearance to that of Ganymede, but the satellite was too far from the spacecraft to provide a satisfactory picture (Figure 6-6), although bright and dark regions can be distinguished on the image. Pioneer 11 also obtained spin-scan images of several of the Galilean satellites (see Chapter 9) which reveal surface markings.

The satellite Io appears to be quite different from the other Jovian satellites. Almost as large as the planet Mercury, Io was known to be orange in color and one of the most reflective objects in the Solar System. Dark polar caps were also seen. The phenomenal brilliance of Io may be due to an extensive crystalline layer much like salt flats in the American West. Sodium vapor emissions were detected from Earth and showed to be from a cloud of sodium vapor that extends 16,000 km (10,000 mi.) from Io's surface. This sodium may originate from the salts deposited on the surface of Io when water from its interior evaporated into space. The sodium may be removed from the surface by the impact of high energy particles trapped in the magnetosphere of Jupiter and intercepted by Io in its orbit around the giant planet.

During an occultation of Pioneer 10 by Io, the radio waves traveling from the spacecraft to Earth probed the atmosphere of Io. They showed that it has a density of some 20,000 times less than that of the Earth's, but it extends some 115 km (70 mi.) above the surface of Io. This satellite is thus one of the smallest planetary bodies known to possess an atmosphere.

An ionosphere was discovered on Io which extends 700 km (420 mi.) high above the dayside of the small satellite. Io is revealed as a unique planetary body in that it possesses an ionosphere while buried in the magnetic field of its mother planet. The ionosphere of Io is affected by the magnetic field of Jupiter to produce quite different day and night aspects. It is theorized that the higher levels of the ionosphere are swept away by the magnetic field of Jupiter. So, at night, when sunlight is not affecting Io's ionosphere, the upper layers decay. This is quite different from Earth, where the lower ionosphere layers decay at night.

The ionospheric density varies from 60,000 electrons per cubic centimeter on the day side to 9,000 on the night side. The unusual density and extent suggest an unusual gas mixture, possibly of sodium, hydrogen, and nitrogen.

Pioneer 10 also found that Io is embedded in a cloud of hydrogen that extends a third of the way around its orbit. This was quite unexpected. Perhaps 161,000 km (100,000 mi.) wide and the same high, the cloud is 805,000 km (500,000 mi.) long, and resembles one-third of a doughnut moving in orbit around Jupiter at a distance of 402,000 km (250,000 mi.) from the planet. No similar hydrogen clouds were detected for the other large satellites though looked for by Pioneer 11 following the Pioneer 10 discovery.

Like the Earth, Jupiter has a bow shock wave which is produced when the high speed solar wind, carrying a magnetic field, interacts with the magnetic field of Jupiter (Figure 6-7). The solar wind is abruptly slowed down so that its effective tempera-

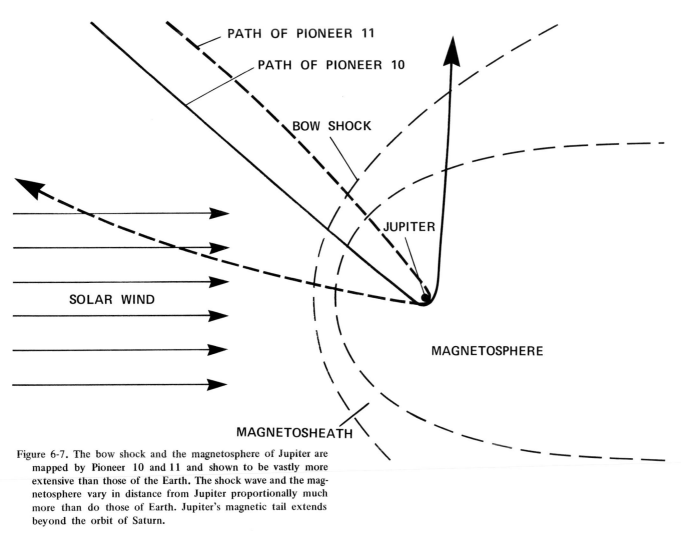

Figure 6-7. The bow shock and the magnetosphere of Jupiter are mapped by Pioneer 10 and 11 and shown to be vastly more extensive than those of the Earth. The shock wave and the magnetosphere vary in distance from Jupiter proportionally much more than do those of Earth. Jupiter's magnetic tail extends beyond the orbit of Saturn.

ture is increased ten times. A magnetosphere surrounds Jupiter just as one surrounds Earth. This protects the planet from the solar wind which cannot penetrate into the magnetosphere. Between the magnetosphere and the bow shock is a turbulent region — the magnetosheath — in which the solar wind is deflected around the magnetosphere: but these phenomena are experienced around Jupiter on a scale vastly greater than around Earth.

Jupiter's magnetosphere has a diameter such that, if it could be seen around Jupiter from Earth, it would be about the apparent diameter of the Moon or Sun in Earth's sky. Pioneer 10's crossings of Jupiter's bow shock show a wave that is over 26 million km (16 million mi.) "wide" in the ecliptic plane, or about 80 percent of the distance between the orbits of Earth and Venus. Jupiter's magnetic tail reaches beyond the orbit of Saturn. The Jovian system is on a truly gigantic scale by earthly standards.

Pioneer 11 discovered that the magnetosphere is blunt on the sunward side and extends at least 80 radii of Jupiter in a vertical direction above and below the planet.

Jupiter's magnetosphere rotates at several hundred thousand miles per hour, along with the planet, and consists of an inner region shaped something like a doughnut with Jupiter in the hole. Outside of the doughnut is a highly unstable outer region caused by ionized gas perhaps thrown out into space as a consequence of the planet's rapid rotation coupled with the changing pressure of the solar wind.

The magnetosphere might also be described as being spongy since it pulsates in the solar wind and often shrinks to half its size. Pioneer 10 crossed the sharply defined boundary of the magnetosphere at 6.8 million km (4.2 million mi.) from Jupiter. Then, as the magnetosphere abruptly changed size, Pioneer's instruments again sensed leaving the magnetosphere and entering it again later, all happening while the spacecraft continued its journey toward the planet. Pioneer 10 actually crossed this constantly pulsating bow shock wave 17 times on the post-encounter trajectory away from Jupiter,

as the configuration of the bow shock changed due to its interaction with changes in the solar wind.

Pioneer 11 recorded three crossings of the bow shock on the inbound trajectory and three outbound. Again, the multiple bow shock and magnetopause crossings during the Pioneer 11 flyby suggest that there is a very dynamic interaction between the solar wind and the magnetosphere.

The Pioneer results show that there are three distinct regions of the Jovian magnetosphere (Figure 6-8): an inner magnetosphere within about 20 radii of Jupiter where the magnetic field of Jupiter predominates; a middle magnetosphere from 20 to 60 Jupiter radii where the magnetic field of the planet is severely distorted by trapped energetic particles; and an outer magnetosphere, beyond 60 Jupiter radii, which exhibits significant irregularities in both the magnitude and direction of the magnetic field.

In the middle magnetosphere, ionized particles form an electric current sheet around Jupiter. In turn, this current flow produces magnetic fields which at large distances from the planet are greater than the magnetic field of Jupiter itself. While in the inner magnetosphere the magnetic field directs particles along the magnetic equator, in the middle field the particles are in control and move parallel to the rotational equator of the planet itself.

At times, when the solar wind affects the magnetosphere, the outer field collapses and accelerates low energy particles to such high velocities that they are squirted out like jets from Jupiter; a new discovery by Pioneer. These particle jets make Jupiter a second source of high energy particle radiation in the Solar System, the other source being the Sun. Pioneer 10 detected these particles 225 million km (140 million mi.) away from Jupiter, and scientists have now confirmed that the particles have been detected at Earth's orbit for several years, but before Pioneer 10, scientists did not know that the particles originated at Jupiter.

The Pioneers refined all the Earth-based predictions. Jupiter's magnetic field is now known to be over 10 times as strong as Earth's field, with the

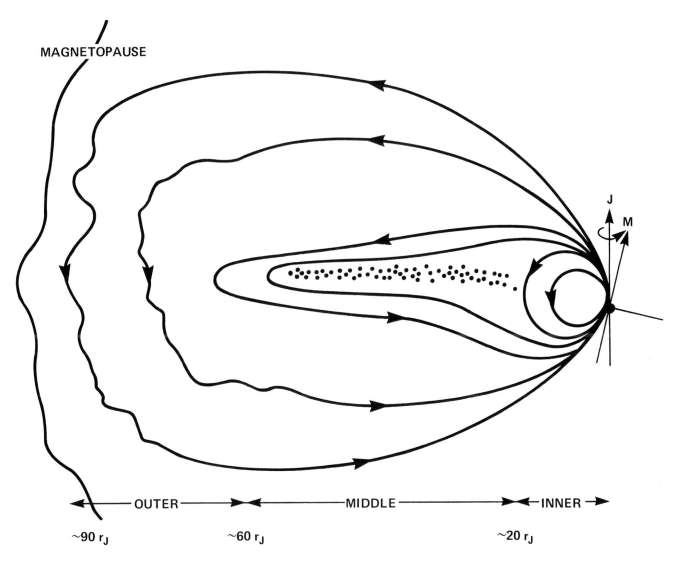

MAGNETOPAUSE

OUTER — MIDDLE — INNER

~90 r$_J$ — ~60 r$_J$ — ~20 r$_J$

Figure 6-8. Jupiter's magnetosphere is differently shaped from that of Earth and has three distinct regions.

total energy in the field being some 20,000 times that in the Earth's field.

The closer and highly inclined trajectory of Pioneer 11 produced a more precise and more detailed definition of the magnetic field of Jupiter. It was found to be 5 percent greater than that estimated from the Pioneer 10 measurements; the dipole moment produces a field which is a measure of source strength of 4.2 Gauss at the visible surface.

Jupiter's field is tilted almost 11 degrees to the planet's axis of rotation, and the center of the field does not coincide with the center of Jupiter but is offset from the spin axis twice as much as Earth's

field is offset. Because of this offset the strength of the field emerging from the cloud tops of Jupiter is quite variable from 14 to 11 Gauss respectively in the north and south polar regions, compared with Earth's polar field of 0.5 Gauss. The poles of Jupiter's field are reversed compared with those of the Earth. A north-seeking compass would point south on Jupiter.

Closer than about three Jupiter radii the magnetic field appears to be more complex than a simple dipole field. These complexities may arise from complex circulation patterns within the metallic hydrogen bulk of the planet.

105

The measurements made by Pioneer 11 revealed that the main magnetic field is somewhat more complex than the Earth's magnetic field. The magnetometer results fit a model in which the quadrupole and octupole moments are at least 20 percent of the dipole moment compared with only about 11 percent for the Earth.

The field is not symmetrical and it has been suggested that this distorts the motion of trapped particles forming the radiation belts and may be the cause of the periodic escape of relativistic electrons from Jupiter into interplanetary space. The concentration of field lines around the strong north pole is also speculated as playing an important role in the modulation of the decametric radiation by the satellite Io. The primary source of decametric radiation might be sporadic precipitation of particles into the northern hemisphere along the flux tube to Io.

The somewhat larger quadrupole and octupole moments present in the magnetic field of Jupiter could have significant implications about the interior of the planet, assuming that the field is generated by a dynamo as generally accepted today. The higher field strength compared to Earth would imply that the dynamo-producing core of Jupiter, i.e., the metallic hydrogen, is responsible for the field rather than a small core of metals and silicates. To produce larger quadrupole and octupole effects the internal core would have to be proportionately larger for Jupiter than for Earth. This could not be a core like that of the Earth.

Energetic particles are trapped in the magnetosphere of Jupiter and produce radiation belts as in Earth's magnetosphere (Figure 6-9). These radiation belts were known before Pioneer 10's flight because of the radio waves generated by them and received at Earth. Such radiation belts require that a planet should have a magnetic field. In fact, their presence led scientists to predict that Jupiter had a magnetic field, although its strength was uncertain before the Pioneer mission made direct measurements within the field.

Because of the tilted magnetic field, the radiation belts of Jupiter are also tilted and wobble up and down in the surrounding space as Jupiter rotates on its axis. So a spacecraft passing the planet moves in and out of the belts due to this wobble.

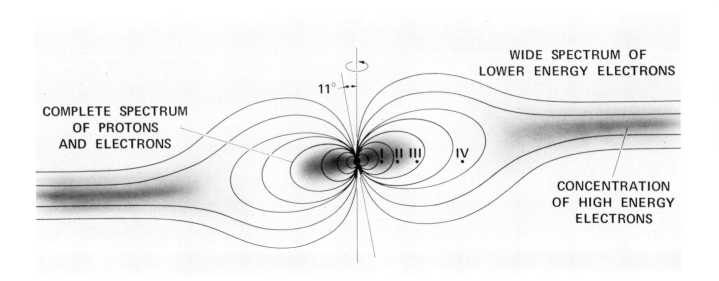

Figure 6-9. Radiation belts consist of particles trapped in Jupiter's magnetic field, and the satellites sweep up many of the charged particles.

The inner belt, consisting of a wide spectrum of energies of electrons and protons, forms a doughnut around the planet, corresponding generally with the classical dipole magnetic field shape extending to about 10 Jupiter radii. Prior to the Pioneer observations it was generally assumed that the trapped radiation originated from the solar wind. Pioneer 11 experiments, however, led to the conclusion that the particles in this inner magnetosphere may not be captured from the solar wind but instead originate from Jupiter.

An outer belt is also spread widely, but with its most energetic particles — high energy electrons — concentrated into a flatter area. This outer belt extends to at least 100 planetary radii parallel to the planet's rotational equatorial plane.

Peak intensities of electrons in the belts, as measured by Pioneer 10, were 10,000 times greater than Earth's maximum. Protons were several thousand times as intense as Earth's belts. The inner radiation belts of Jupiter, as measured by Pioneer 10, had the highest radiation intensity so far measured; comparable to radiation intensities following an explosion of a nuclear device in the upper atmosphere.

Pioneer 11 confirmed these high intensities. In the inner region of the magnetosphere high energy protons exceeding 35 MeV appear to peak in two shells; the outer shell was detected at 3.5 Jovian radii by Pioneer 10, and confirmed by Pioneer 11, and an inner shell, discovered by Pioneer 11, has a peak at 1.78 radii of Jupiter. Pioneer 11 also found that there is a greater flux of energetic particles at high Jovian latitudes than would have been expected from the measurements made by Pioneer 10. It also discovered that the flux of energetic particles peaks on either side of the dipole magnetic equator.

An important discovery of Pioneer 10 was that Jupiter releases bursts of very energetic electrons into interplanetary space. Pioneer 11 also detected the electrons and discovered that they were in phase with the observations made previously by Pioneer 10. Two days before Pioneer 11 entered the magnetosphere of Jupiter the spacecraft's instruments began to detect bursts of low energy protons. Both electrons and protons are emitted in phase with the synodic rotation of Jupiter.

Jupiter has thus been found to be a new source of energetic particles in interplanetary space which scientists can use to study particle propagation in the solar wind. Figure 6-10 shows the increasing rate of energetic electron events derived from the helium vector magnetometer results as Pioneer 10 approached Jupiter while Pioneer 11, still far from the planet, saw many fewer electron events. These events are observed when the interplanetary magnetic field provides good connection between Jupiter and the spacecraft. Large amplitude waves in the magnetic field have been found associated with the electrons in interplanetary space. They are probably generated by the electrons. Figure 6-11 shows diagrammatically the relation of the spacecraft, Jupiter, the interplanetary magnetic field, and the magnetic waves during a Jovian interplanetary electron event. Since cosmic rays are probably confined to the galaxy by similar self-generated waves, this observation by the Pioneers has significance for galactic as well as interplanetary physics.

In addition to 10-hour variations in the electron intensity and spectrum observed inside Jupiter's magnetosphere, similar variations were observed as far as 150 million km (93 million mi.) from the planet. These variations are in phase with those observed inside Jupiter's magnetosphere as shown in Figure 6-12. Both inside and outside of the magnetosphere the variations appear to be locked in phase; i.e., they occur regularly every 10 hours at precisely the same time irrespective of distance from the planet.

Comparison of the timing of the 10 hour intensity and spectral variations observed in the energetic electron flux in Jupiter's outer magnetosphere and in interplanetary space has caused scientists to reexamine the idea that the variations are caused by the flapping of the outer magnetosphere and equatorial current sheet in the course of Jupiter's rotation. Instead, the data now suggest that the variations take place simultaneously in the whole outer magnetosphere, so that Jupiter

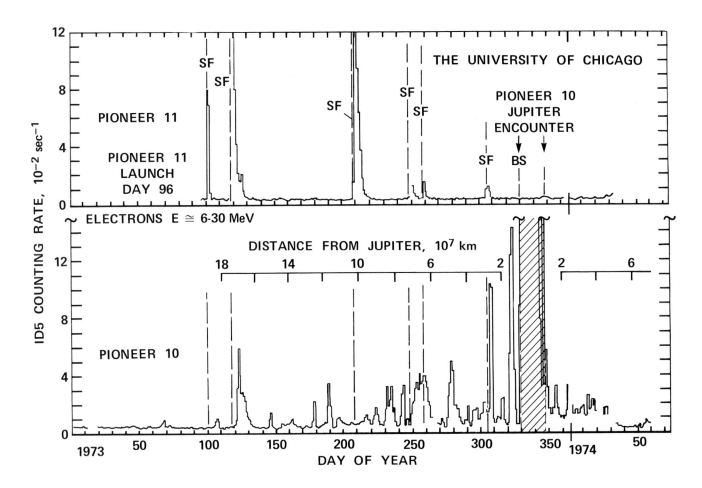

Figure 6-10. Comparisons of the number of energetic electron events observed by Pioneer 10 and Pioneer 11 during the encounter of Pioneer 10.

resembles a blinking beacon more than a twirling floppy hat as originally suggested from the Pioneer 10 data.

The results of Pioneer 11 suggest that the model of Jupiter's trapped radiation in the middle and outer magnetosphere is best represented by a disc with the magnetic field lines near the magnetic equator being closed and hence capable of trapping charged particles out to a radius of 100 times that of Jupiter.

It is also now clear that the magnetosphere is quite blunted on the sunward side of the planet. No information was available from either Pioneer 10 or 11 on the shape on the anti-solar side of Jupiter. Pioneer 10 did, however, encounter

phenomena suggestive of a magnetic tail of Jupiter extending beyond the orbit of Saturn.

A significant new finding from the Pioneer 11 observations is that there is a net streaming of both electrons and protons away from the planet along high latitude field lines. The electrons were at energies less than 40 keV and less than 560 keV, and the protons between 0.61 and 3.41 MeV.

A recirculation of energetic particles within the Jovian magnetosphere thus emerges as a dynamic feature of Jupiter. It also suggests that the emission of energetic particles into interplanetary space — as observed by both Pioneers — may take place from the poles and other latitudes rather than exclusively from the equatorial regions of the magnetosphere.

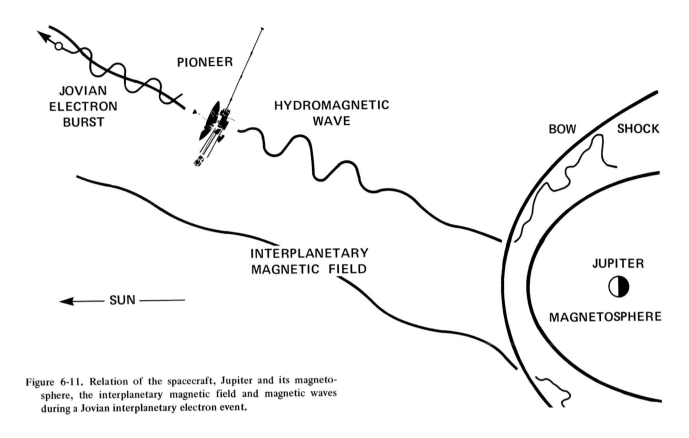

Figure 6-11. Relation of the spacecraft, Jupiter and its magnetosphere, the interplanetary magnetic field and magnetic waves
during a Jovian interplanetary electron event.

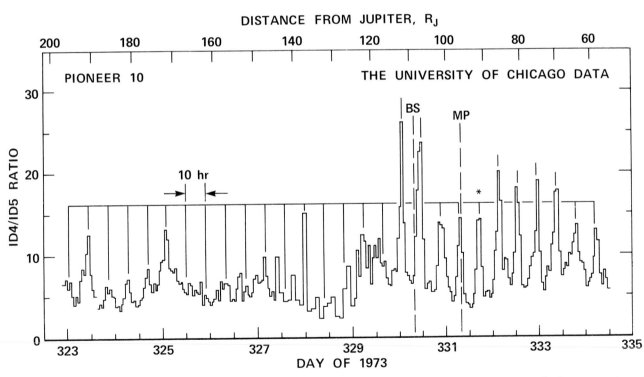

Figure 6-12. Both inside and outside of Jupiter's magnetosphere, the
10-hour modulation of electron intensity appears to be in phase.
BS is the bow shock. MP is the magnetopause.

Particles may be transported from low to high latitudes without significant changes to their energy. Particles in the outer magnetodisc diffusing inwards toward Jupiter are eventually squeezed into a pancake-shaped volume in the inner magnetosphere. Apparently the particles interact with plasma waves generated inside the magnetosphere which cause the particles to escape from the pancake-shaped magnetodisc and reach low altitudes. It is at these low altitudes that they can be transported to high latitudes without significant change in energy. The particles are thereby injected onto high latitude field lines and provide the outward streaming high latitude flux observed by Pioneer 11 (Figure 6-13). This dynamic recirculation may explain the otherwise baffling problem of the presence of particles with megavolt energies in the region of the outer magnetosphere including its boundary.

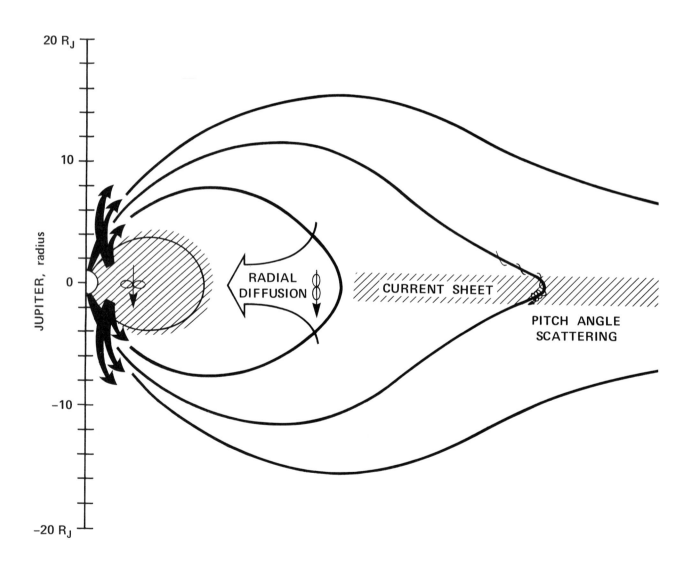

Figure 6-13. Energetic particles appear to be circulating in the magnetosphere and ejected at high latitudes.

110

Also this process may explain why the 10-hour periodicity occurs rather than a 5-hour periodicity that would be expected if the energetic particles from Jupiter observed in interplanetary space were squirted from the equatorial regions. The interplanetary magnetic field at a particular point in space would be expected to connect to either the north or south polar regions of Jupiter at any given time. Energetic particles originating from these regions by the circulation process would be modulated by planetary rotation so as to show a 10-hour periodicity. Thus the process of cross field diffusion and escape of particles from the polar regions may account for the 10-hour periodicity observed by the Pioneer spacecraft. However, a 5-hour periodicity could have been missed by both Pioneer spacecraft because of their trajectories.

The dynamics of the Jovian magnetosphere with its charged particles appear to differ in important ways from those of the Earth. First the presence of substantial intensities of electrons having energies greater than 20 MeV in the outer magnetosphere cannot be explained by trapping of particles from the solar wind. Such solar wind particles could only reach about 1 keV. The corotation of energetic particles with Jupiter persists out to the magnetopause, whereas for the Earth corotation terminates at the outer boundary of the plasmasphere, far inside the magnetopause. The inner satellites, Amalthea, Io, Europa, and Ganymede, produce a fluctuating and complex structure of energetic particles. By contrast, the Earth's Moon is far outside Earth's magnetosphere.

It seems likely that the capture of solar wind particles may be a relatively minor feature of the dynamics of the Jovian magnetosphere, whereas the internal acceleration of particles internally available within the magnetosphere may be the dominant process. Nevertheless, whether or not the solar wind particles are captured within the system, the solar wind is essential to establishing the physical conditions under which transfer of rotational energy from Jupiter to the charged particles can take place. The flow of the solar wind past Jupiter generates the axially asymmetric and non-rotating situation that is essential for the development of the Jovian magnetosphere.

While Earth's Moon is far beyond Earth's radiation belts, the large satellites of Jupiter and the innermost known satellite, Amalthea, are immersed in the Jovian belts. Consequently, the satellites sweep up particles from the belts and remove high energy particles to reduce total radiation near Jupiter by as much as 100 times. By far the largest number of particles is removed by Io. Additionally, this satellite is known to accelerate particles and to induce, in some way, the emission of decametric radio waves. Within the orbit of Amalthea the radiation environment is extremely complex and the flux of energetic particles varies from place to place around Jupiter. There appear to be nodes of concentrated particles and no single maximum. Indeed, the effect of Amalthea may be what causes the flux of energetic particles to stop increasing closer to Jupiter. However, there is the possibility that other effects may be controlling the number of particles close in to the planet as well as Amalthea's sweeping action. The offset of the magnetic field creates a particle-free region between the cloud surface of the planet and one-tenth of a radii above it analogous to an eccentric cam action.

Pioneer 11 measured large reductions in electron flux for energies below 560 keV and in proton flux for energies around 2.1 MeV as the spacecraft crossed the orbit of Io. Smaller effects were observed at the orbit of Amalthea, and only a rather feeble effect was seen at the orbit of Europa. However, near the orbit of Ganymede, Pioneer 11 detected strong transient anisotropic bursts of 1 MeV protons. One sequence of one-minute bursts continued for several hours. These particles appear to be locally accelerated.

The Pioneer 11 spacecraft discovered a high electron current flow at the orbit of Ganymede. Such an increase in electron flow had not been observed at the other passages of the Pioneers through satellite orbits. Near the Io flux tube — the magnetic field line of Jupiter extending to Io along which scientists had speculated that large currents should flow — Pioneer 11 detected an increase of about ten times the flux of electrons with energies above 0.46 MeV.

The picture of Jupiter emerges as an enormous spinning magnetosphere buffeted by the solar wind, a magnetosphere that is continually stirred and mixed by the Galilean satellites and Amalthea, a magnetosphere in which processes are at work very different from those taking place in the magnetosphere of Earth. As a result of the encounter of Pioneer 11 in which the total electron dosage was less than that experienced by Pioneer 10 because of the highly inclined trajectory of the second spacecraft even though approaching much closer to Jupiter, spacecraft trajectories can now be planned to pass quickly through the plane of intense radiation. Thus the practicality of the gravity-assist slingshot technique to explore the outer Solar System has been demonstrated and Pioneer 11, now renamed Pioneer Saturn, is on its way to the next outer gas giant with virtually no damage to its electronics or scientific instruments from its close approach to Jupiter.

The Pioneers also permitted a close look at the planet Jupiter itself as well as the environment surrounding it. These close looks were made possible by the spin-scan imaging technique, the infrared and ultraviolet experiments, and the radio occultation experiment. As a result, astronomers have been able to revise theories about the internal composition and the meteorology and atmosphere of the giant planet. The spin-scan images are discussed in detail in Chapters 8 and 9, but it is appropriate here to summarize the current theories of Jupiter which have been strengthened by or have evolved from the Pioneer 10 and 11 results.

Jupiter appears to be almost entirely fluid, with possibly only a very small solid core (Figure 6-14). This liquid interior seethes with internal heat energy being transferred from deep within the planet to its outer regions.

Jupiter's center may be at a temperature of 30,000° C (54,000° F); heat from continued gravitational contraction and partly residual primordial heat. Since the temperature at the cloud

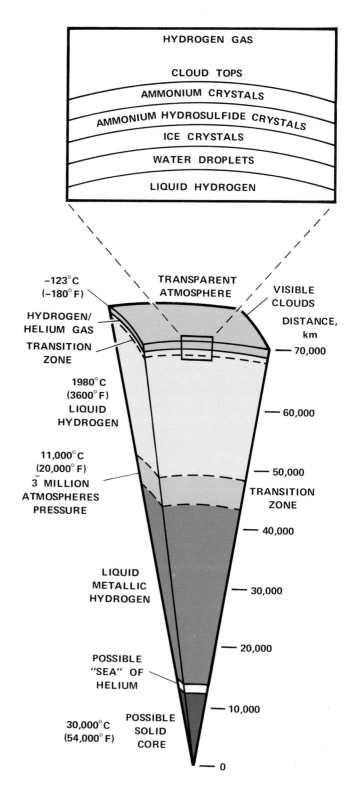

Figure 6-14. Pioneer 10 confirms models of Jupiter that suggest the planet is nearly all liquid with a very small core and a deep atmosphere.

112

tops of Jupiter is around $-123°$ C ($-190°$ F), there is a large range of temperatures within the planet and millions of cubic miles of the atmosphere could be at room temperature.

Atop the main liquid bulk of the planet is an even more turbulent atmosphere, possibly 970 km (600 mi.) thick. The top regions of this atmosphere produce clouds which are the visible surface seen from Earth. A transparent atmosphere extends above the visible surface and ultimately leads to a multi-layered ionosphere of highly rarefied, electrically charged gas.

Jupiter has convective circulation patterns, but the rapid rotation and the flow of internal energy outwards makes the weather patterns very different from Earth's.

Measurements of the density distribution within Jupiter from the paths of the Pioneers as they flew by imply that the planet is largely liquid; it has no concentrations of mass and no detectable crust or solid surface. But Jupiter could still possess a small rocky core of a few Earth masses consisting of iron and silicates. The composition of Jupiter is not precisely like that of the Sun since there is a five-fold enhancement of heavy materials probably in the form of silicates and the ices of ammonia, methane and water. Scientists cannot yet define how these heavier materials are distributed throughout the planet.

Jupiter is probably 87 percent hydrogen, and this hydrogen is most likely liquid, not solid, at the high internal temperatures of Jupiter, despite the high internal pressures. However, the pressure within Jupiter at about 24,000 km (15,000 mi.) below the visible cloud tops is sufficient to convert liquid hydrogen into a metallic form which more readily conducts heat and electricity.

Temperatures and pressures are enormously high in the interior of Jupiter. At 970 km (600 mi.) below the cloud tops the temperature is probably about 2000° C (3600° F). At 2900 km (1800 mi.), the temperature is believed to be 6000° C (11,000° F). At 24,000 km (15,000 mi.), the temperature may reach 11,000° C (20,000° F), and the pressure three million Earth atmospheres. It is

about this level that the liquid hydrogen should turn into liquid metallic hydrogen.

Jupiter also consists of at least 12 percent helium. This helium might theoretically be soluble in liquid hydrogen. It is speculated, however, that if conditions are not just right, the helium might be insoluble within the hydrogen and form a 'sea' around the central core of Jupiter on top of which the liquid metallic hydrogen would float. There is, however, no adequate theory yet on the miscibility of metallic hydrogen and helium within a planet such as Jupiter. There might be precipitation of helium in the molecular hydrogen which would be important to layering and convective processes within the planet. In turn these could affect the magnetic field. Additionally there is the question as to whether rocks might dissolve in a hydrogen/helium mixture at high temperature. This could prevent the formation of a discrete rocky core or disperse such a core that had already formed early in the planet's history.

The internal structure of Jupiter still remains somewhat indistinct.

The seething activity in the metallic hydrogen of Jupiter is thought to be evidenced by the complex magnetic field of the planet. Hydrogen moving up from the center of Jupiter, like water coming to a boil in a saucepan, would produce eddy currents that give rise to the magnetic field through rotation of the planet.

Somewhere around 970 km (600 mi.) below the cloud tops, where the pressure is low enough for the liquid hydrogen to become a gas the atmosphere of Jupiter begins. It is unlikely, however, that there is a sharp transition surface similar to the surface of an ocean. Rather, there is most probably a gradual change through a mixture of gas and liquid. But the top 970 km (600 mi.) of the planet, where there is no longer hydrogen in liquid form, is defined as the atmosphere of Jupiter.

Jupiter's atmosphere accounts for about 1 percent of the mass of the planet. It is predominantly hydrogen (about 85 percent) with nearly 15 percent helium and less than 1 percent of other gases. This is the same as the proportions of elements found in the Sun. Although helium was believed to be present on Jupiter, the gas was not positively identified there until Pioneer 10 made its experiments.

Jupiter's atmosphere also has small amounts of ammonia and methane and traces of deuterium, acetylene, ethane and phosphine. In recent years water vapor has been detected in small quantities and also carbon monoxide, hydrogen cyanide, and germane. Several of the trace gases have been discovered, and continue to be discovered, through the use of telescopes mounted on high flying air-

craft that overcome some of the masking absorptions of the Earth's atmosphere.

In the regions of the atmosphere, 32 km (20 mi.) or so above and below the cloud tops, solar heat as well as the internal heat from Jupiter flowing outwards affects circulation. Jupiter's clouds form in the atmosphere by condensation as on Earth. But Jupiter's clouds appear to be of ammonia and ammonia compounds as well as water. The topmost clouds are thought to be of ammonia crystals with water clouds confined to lower levels.

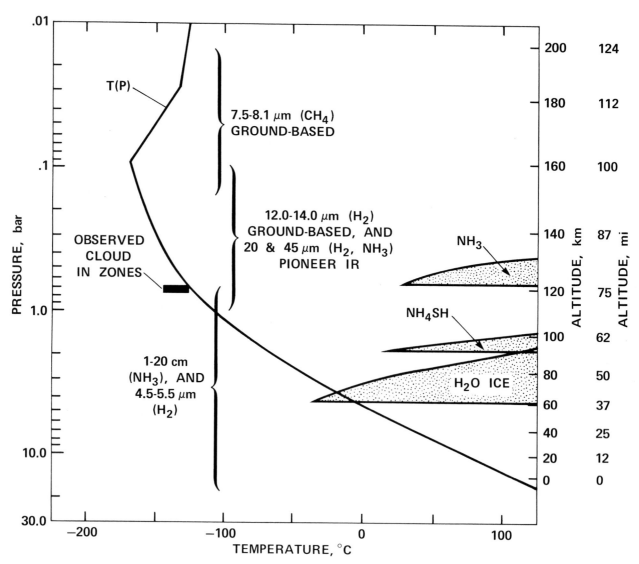

Figure 6-15. The temperature profile in the atmosphere of Jupiter and the location of various cloud layers are shown in this diagram from data of A. Ingersoll, Caltech.

An inversion layer 35 km (22 mi.) above the visible clouds is thought to be caused by a layer of aerosols and hydrocarbons such as ethane and acetylene. This is a layer where sunlight is absorbed and adds heat to the cooling atmosphere. Methane, too, would absorb sunlight and contribute to the inversion layer.

Pioneer 10's occultation experiment produced results for the temperature of the Jovian atmosphere in conflict with ground based observations. And the data for Pioneer 11 were consistent with those from Pioneer 10. They were finally matched with the ground based observations by taking into account the great oblateness, or spin flattening, of Jupiter and its effect upon the path of the radio waves through the Jovian atmosphere. For three measurements — entry and exit of Pioneer 10, and exit of Pioneer 11 — the occultation data are quite consistent. They show a temperature inversion between the 10 and 100 millibar levels, with temperatures between −133 and −113° C (−207 and −171° F) at the 10 millibar level and −183 to −163° C (−297 to −261° F) at 100 millibars. At the 0.001 millibar level, the temperature of the Jovian atmosphere, determined by an occultation of Beta Scorpio, is about −103° C (−153° F); at the cloud tops, however, the temperature is about −148° C (−234° F) (Figure 6-15).

The Pioneer observations also show that the poles and the equatorial regions of Jupiter have effectively the same temperature; the temperature is also the same on north and south hemispheres and the day and night sides. Also, because the axis of Jupiter is inclined by only a few degrees, the planet does not have seasons like those of the Earth.

Because the Sun's radiation falls more concentrated per unit area of the equatorial regions it would be expected that the equator would be warmer than the poles as on Earth and other planets. Two theories have been proposed to account for the even distribution of temperature measured by infrared radiation from Jupiter. The first says the circulation within the atmosphere should be very efficient to redistribute the solar heat. The second suggests that the heat flux from inside Jupiter is sufficiently greater at the poles to balance the lesser solar input there. Since there is no equator to pole atmospheric flow pattern observed on Jupiter, the second theory seems more likely to fit conditions on the giant planet. It is believed that convection is so effective over the whole planet that it eliminates any temperature differences due to the solar input variations with latitude. Thus, at the poles, where the cloud temperatures would expect to fall, convection speeds up from the interior to bring up heat and keep the temperature constant. At the equator, where the clouds are warmed more by the Sun, the amount of convection is reduced. Thus the planet acts as though governed by a huge thermostat.

It has been speculated that spots on Jupiter, including the Great Red Spot, are most probably large hurricane-type features consisting of groups of persistent rising air masses like gigantic thunderstorms (Figure 6-16). It is no longer believed that the Great Red Spot is a column of gas anchored to some feature on a hypothetical surface of Jupiter. The core of the planet is now believed to be much too small to produce effects that would extend to the visible surface of the clouds; and the Pioneer spacecraft revealed no noticeable density differences that could be interpreted as being caused by the Red Spot extending toward a core.

Fundamental questions such as what makes the spot red and why has it lasted so long still remain unanswered though there are new speculative theories. Theories about the cause of the spot — that it is the upper atmospheric manifestation of a surface feature or a floating island — are giving way to hydrodynamic explanations. Even the concept of it being the Jovian equivalent of a hurricane is being doubted. Equations describing the atmospheric flow on a rapidly rotating planet with an internal heat source can now be solved by the newest computers. Several scientists have developed mathematical models to explain the Great Red Spot. Whether these new hydrodynamic solutions do in fact apply to the real red spot must await careful comparison of the predictions of the spot's

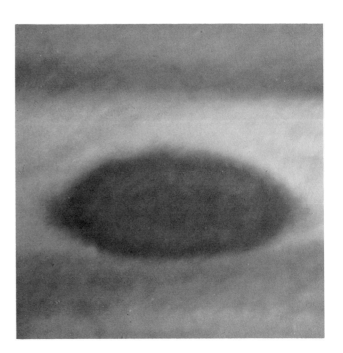

Figure 6-16. The Great Red Spot is probably a hurricane-like almost permanent feature consisting of a great system of thunderstorms rising several kilometers above the topmost clouds of Jupiter.

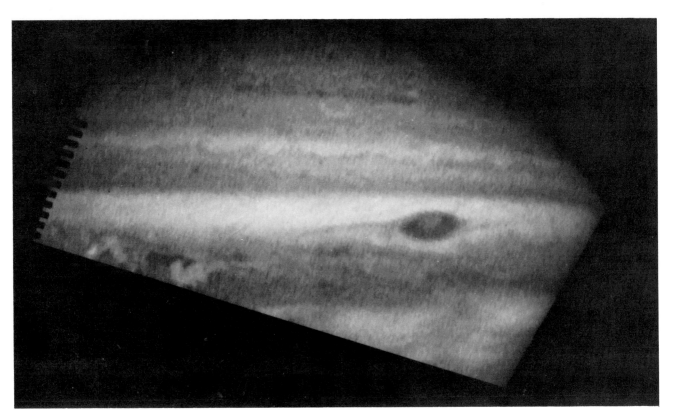

Figure 6-17. A northern red spot on Jupiter, recorded in new detail by Pioneer, lends credence to the view that the red spots are purely atmospheric phenomena.

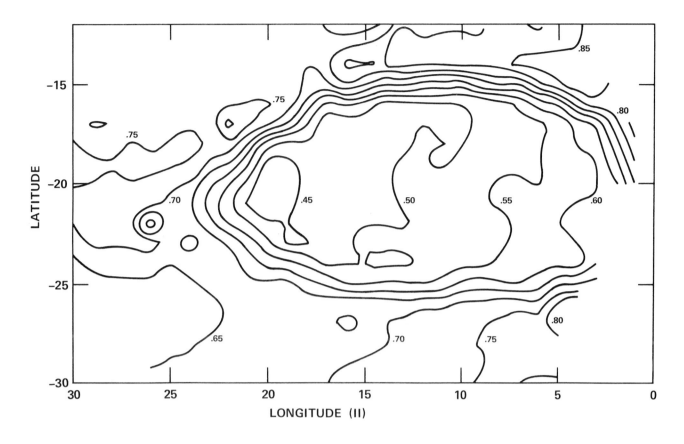

Figure 6-18. Color contours of the Great Red Spot on the terminator show bluing of the light by atmospheric scattering. (*Figure courtesy Lyn Doose.*)

behavior and characteristics with further observations and analysis of the Pioneer pictures.

One of the most significant images from Pioneer 10 showed a similar spot, though much smaller, in the Northern Hemisphere at the same latitude as the Great Red Spot (Figure 6-17). It has the same shape and structure and implies that the red spots are meteorological features in the atmosphere.

The Great Red Spot appears to rotate counterclockwise as seen from above, it is anticyclonic and behaves as an ascending mass of gas flowing out at the level of its top which pokes several miles above the topmost cloud layers.

By looking at sunlight reflected off a cloud, it is difficult to tell even on Earth, what is under the cloud. But we can determine something from the reflected light, about the size, distribution, and refractive index of the droplets making up the cloud. There is no haze over the Red Spot as it is carried by the rotation of Jupiter across the limb. At the terminator, the Red Spot shows bluing of the reflected light, where there is scattering of the sunlight into space (Figure 6-18).

117

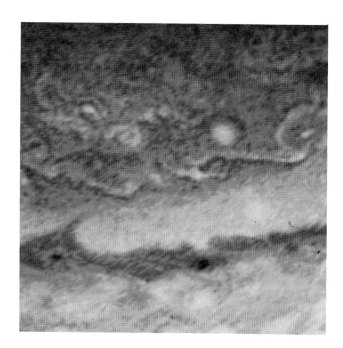
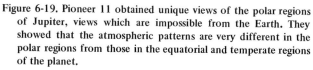

Figure 6-19. Pioneer 11 obtained unique views of the polar regions of Jupiter, views which are impossible from the Earth. They showed that the atmospheric patterns are very different in the polar regions from those in the equatorial and temperate regions of the planet.

Scientists speculate that the red color of the spot may be a result of phosphine being carried to great heights and broken down by solar ultraviolet to produce red phosphorous. Very high clouds would thus be red on Jupiter.

The views of the north polar regions of Jupiter (Figure 6-19) were unique in that such views of the planet cannot be obtained from the Earth. North of the North Temperate Belt, Pioneer's pictures show that the dark belts and light zones characteristic of the equatorial regions are successively less organized. The banded structure changes into oval and circular features within 10 to 15 degrees of the pole.

The details are greater in the red images of the polar regions, thereby suggesting that the atmosphere is thicker above the polar clouds than over the temperate and equatorial clouds of the planet.

Photopolarimetry has been used to estimate the optical depth of the atmosphere above the cloud tops. It appears to be three times as great above

60° latitude than in the equatorial zone. But the effects may arise from a thin high cloud layer or an unknown absorption in the upper atmosphere.

We are just beginning to understand the atmospheric dynamics of cloudy planets, and the Pioneer observations of Jupiter add considerably to our basic knowledge, by providing information on very deep atmospheres in rapid rotation without any solid surface interactions with the atmosphere. It also provides information on atmospheres driven mainly by heat from below rather than from the Sun.

Pioneer results seem to confirm earlier theoretical deductions that the Red Spot and the light colored zones are regions of well developed clouds, swirling anti-cyclones and rising air masses. The darker belts, by contrast, are cyclonic, sinking masses of air leading to depressed clouds. The ways in which the belts and zones scatter sunlight reflected from them are very different. It is speculated that the belts may appear dark because of

118

dark aerosols suspended in the gaseous atmosphere there. On Jupiter the familiar cyclones and anti-cyclones of Earth are stretched into linear or hook-shaped features on the rapidly rotating planet, with extremely turbulent areas separating adjacent bands of different velocities; areas in which there are many examples of classical von Karman vortices.

Whereas storm systems on Earth last for several days or for several weeks, as a moving system such as a hurricane, such storm systems on Jupiter last for very long periods. The Great Red Spot, for example, has been observed for centuries. On Earth, there are strong interactions between the atmospheric systems and the land masses over which they travel. These tend to break up the atmospheric system. In addition, the Earth systems are powered by solar heat concentrated in the tropics during the daytime. Thus, they tend to break up when they move away from the tropics and into the night hemisphere of Earth. Again, Jupiter is different since its storms are powered mainly by internal heat flow which is more evenly distributed planetwide and over the day and night hemispheres. It is because of the internal heat source that Jupiter weather systems can last for long periods of time.

Some of the bright zones on Jupiter (Figure 6-20) may be analogous to the tropical convergences on Earth which show up plainly on satellite photographs as bands of thunderstorms, a few degrees north and south of the equator. They are

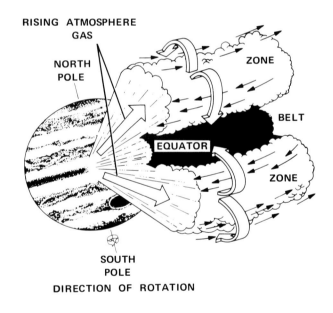

Figure 6-20. Some of the bright zones of Jupiter may be analogous to the tropical convergences on Earth weather patterns around the planet.

119

caused on Earth by the trade winds, blowing toward the equator, and rising moist air in the tropics. The consequent thunderstorms spread their tops into cirrus clouds which then flow back toward the poles. Similarly, on Jupiter, rising air masses may produce great masses of cumulus clouds which spread into anvil shapes and give rise to the bright bands of the north tropical and south tropical zones.

A problem still not resolved is why, when ammonia and water are both colorless when condensed, Jupiter displays bands of colored clouds and the red spots. Certain ammonia compounds produce colors like those on Jupiter given sufficient exposure to ultraviolet radiation, and sufficient solar ultraviolet radiation does penetrate to the cloud levels. It may possibly be that carbon compounds or traces of sulfur and phosphorous — all believed to be present in primordial material — supply some of the color. Only traces would be needed to react in sunlight and produce the types of colors seen on Jupiter. It could very well be that because the gas of the Great Red Spot rises so high, it is subject to irradiation by solar ultraviolet which triggers a different set of photochemical reactions to deepen the color.

Since solar ultraviolet radiation penetrates to lower cloud levels, i.e., the belts, the Great Red Spot may be due to a different type of chemical reaction, temperature, or longer exposure to ultraviolet radiation because its gases experience less mixing than those in the belts.

Another possible cause of colors on Jupiter could be the presence of free radicals. At very low temperatures such as experienced in the higher cloud layers, chemical compounds can exist with some of their normal complement of atoms missing and still be relatively stable. They are called free radicals and are generally highly colored.

Limb darkening of Jupiter shows that the clouds of the planet consist of a thin upper layer which is semi-transparent to red light above a more dense lower layer. The particles of Jupiter's upper clouds are of much smaller dimensions than particles in Earth's clouds.

The precise modeling of cloud layers of Jupiter is still in progress. Generally, two cloud layers appear to be present; one a thick, low deck above which there is a gaseous atmosphere; two a thin, high layer topped by a layer or layers of aerosols. The Jovian cloud particles are not spherical (unlike the sulfuric acid droplets in the Venus atmosphere that permit precise numerical analysis with existing theory). Instead the Jovian particles are irregular and most probably larger than the wavelength of light. At the poles, the clouds seem to be low. But alternatively the upper cloud layer may be diffuse with many aerosols suspended in the upper atmosphere.

The pictures of Jupiter revealed several surprises about the clouds. The detail cloud structures in intermediate latitudes were unexpected. The billows and whirls near the edges of belts and zones confirmed that there are rapid changes in wind direction and wind speeds there. Motions in latitude as well as in longitude seem to be evidenced by trends and slants in the North Tropical Zone, for example. The plume in the equatorial zone was revealed in remarkable detail which provides structural information important to understanding these common cloud forms of the equatorial zone.

Infrared observations of Jupiter have been made from the ground at wavelengths of 5 micrometers where there is a window of transparency in both the Earth's atmosphere and that of Jupiter, thereby permitting a look deep into the Jovian atmosphere. Maps of Jupiter at this wavelength made by James A. Westphal at the Hale Observatories show belts and zones very much the same as photographs of Jupiter in visible light. But the darker visible belts are light (hotter) in the infrared pictures and the light visible zones are dark (cooler) (Figure 6-21). The infrared radiation comes from deep within the atmosphere and shows that the dark visible belts are lower, or thinner, hotter clouds, while the bright visible features are high, or thicker, cooler clouds. There is also very close correlation between infrared maps of the dark, bluish-gray regions which are interpreted as

120

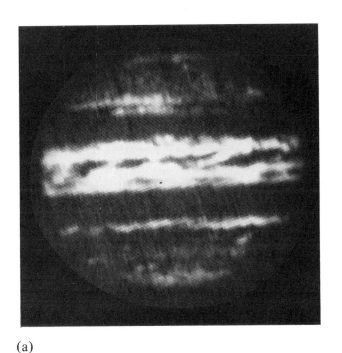

(a)

(b)

Figure 6-21. Ground-based infrared maps of Jupiter show correlation between infrared sources and the dark zones of the planet seen on the Pioneer images. (*Photo: Hale Observatories.*)

dark holes in the clouds. These show as regions of increased infrared radiation. The 5 micrometer pictures also correlate very well with the Pioneer pictures of visible features; the prominent plume and various cells and wave effects are clearly the same.

The Pioneer spacecraft also made infrared maps of Jupiter, but at 20 and 40 micrometers where, although there is less detail because of less penetration and less temperature contrast, the planet emits more infrared radiation than at 5 micrometers (Figure 6-22). These maps also provide confirmation of the high and low clouds and provide information on the general heat balance of the planet. They confirm that Jupiter emits more heat than it receives from the Sun.

Figure 6-22. An infrared map of Jupiter from Pioneer 11 provides information about the heat balance and shows that Jupiter emits 1.9 times as much heat energy as it receives from the Sun.

In spite of the loss of some of the data covering the northern hemisphere of Jupiter when radiation affected the instrument, the infrared radiometer carried by Pioneer 11 provided two infrared spin-scan images of the planet. A complete image was centered at 41° S and a partial image was centered at 52° N latitude on Jupiter. The ratio of total thermal energy to absorbed solar energy was revised to 1.9 ± 0.2 compared with previous estimates of 2.5 ± 0.5. The fact that both Pioneer 10 and Pioneer 11 data yield this result adds confidence in the new value.

Thus, Jupiter does not appear to be emitting as much internal heat as was once thought; about 24 percent less than had been assumed from Earth-based observations.

Jupiter's ionosphere rises 4000 km (2500 mi.) above the visible surface. It is ten times as thick and five times as hot as was predicted. Also, the ionosphere has at least five sharply defined layers of different density, similar to Earth's ionospheric layers that permit long range radio communication around Earth by returning certain radio waves to the ground.

The determination that Jupiter has a warm, extended, hydrogen rich atmosphere has important implications for further exploration of the giant planet.

Prior to measurements by the two Pioneers, it was generally considered that the heating of an entry probe into Jupiter's atmosphere would be greater than could be overcome by present-day technology. Now the new determinations of the Jovian atmosphere suggest that a probe can be made to survive entry into the Jovian atmosphere and measure directly its characteristics and constituents.

Enough has been confirmed or found out about Jupiter by the Pioneers to encourage further exploration. These two spacecraft have also demonstrated that such exploration is quite within the capabilities of present space technology which offers the opportunity now to sample directly what may be primordial material of the Solar System; thus, dipping back four and a half billion years in time.

7

How Pictures Came from Jupiter

As MENTIONED EARLIER, Pioneer 10 and 11 each carried a small but intriguing instrument called the Imaging Photopolarimeter (IPP). This instrument measured the strength of sunlight scattered from the clouds of Jupiter, and converted the information into digital representations of different shades of red and blue that made up each image of Jupiter. This digital information was then transmitted to the Earth as part of the spacecraft telemetry. With the aid of computers, scientists converted these signals into patterns of light and dark on a photographic film; they made unique pictures of Jupiter. This chapter describes the complexities of the process and shows how scientists overcame many of the problems of producing images of the giant planet.

Bits and Pixels

Photographs in newspapers and magazines are reproduced by a half-tone process. If these pictures are enlarged many times, they are seen to be made up of thousands of regularly spaced, little black dots of varying sizes. Dark areas have large dots and light areas have smaller dots. These dots are too small for the unaided eye to separate them, and the viewer sees what appears to be a continuous distribution of changing gray levels that make the picture. The shade of gray is controlled by varying the dot size; small dots give the impression of light gray and large dots form the dark gray areas.

Instead of being made up of dots a picture can consist of small contiguous areas called picture elements, or pixels, each with its own shade of gray. Pixels are usually square or rectangular, and if there are enough shades of gray and if the pixels are small enough, the eye fuses the array of little squares or rectangles into a continuous, smooth-looking picture.

The shades of gray, or gray levels as they are usually called, can also be subdivided into a limited number of different values. A number, say 64, evenly spaced shades of gray are chosen. Black is thus represented by 0, white by 63, and the intermediate shades by numbers 1 through 62.

123

Figure 7-1(a) shows a photograph originally consisting of pixels and gray levels instead of the conventional dots, although reproduced in this book by a dot process. A small portion of the picture shown magnified in Figure 7-1(b) reveals the pixels and the gray levels. The list of numbers, shown on the right (Figure 7-1(c)), corresponds to the gray levels seen in the enlarged part of the picture.

To send pictures, or scenes, from one place to another, the original scene is scanned with an instrument that measures brightness of the light

Figure 7-1. This scan photograph from an ERTS satellite shows the San Francisco Bay Area where Pioneer Mission Control Center is located at Ames Research Center, Moffett Field. (a) Shows the gross view of the whole area. (b) An enlarged view of part of the area to show the runway at San Francisco International Airport. The area covered is designated by the white square on picture (a). The enlargement here shows how the picture consists of discrete squares having different tones of gray. (c) At the right is a computer listing of numbers to identify the value of the gray level of each square.

(a)

124

that is gathered from each of many small areas in the scene. The brightness reading is converted, or coded, into a binary number (a string of zeros and ones, somewhat like the dot-dash nature of the Morse code) and sent by radio or over wires to a distant receiver. There the stream of impulses is converted back to appropriately positioned small gray areas on a film, thus creating a facsimile of the original scene. Processes similar to this have been in use for many decades for wire transmission of newspaper photographs and are known as facsimile systems.

However, prior to this mission to Jupiter, such a system had not been used to obtain images of dis-

tant planets even though it had been proposed for this purpose as long ago as 1953 for a Mars orbiter. Instead, all imaging of planets from spacecraft — except the Earth from Earth satellites — used television or conventional cameras. For many reasons, such as weight and power requirements, it was decided not to use a TV system for Pioneer Jupiter, but rather to apply a well-established alternative method using a spin-scan telescope, a method already used by NOAA satellites to produce weather maps of the Earth.

A more detailed technical description of the imaging photopolarimeter (IPP) used in Pioneer is given in Appendix 1, but basically this is how the instrument operates. A small telescope collects light from a 0.028 degree square (i.e. the equivalent of a one-centimeter square seen at a distance of 20 meters or a one-inch square at 55 yards) located along the direction the telescope is pointing. This direction is called the line of sight. Color filters separate red and blue components of the light, and the strength of these components is then measured electronically.

(b)

9	9	8	8	8	9	11	18	35	45	43	33	42	38	37	43	48	12	9	8
9	9	8	8	8	9	11	25	35	45	35	39	38	34	35	35	39	9	9	8
9	8	7	8	8	9	11	32	37	45	30	44	34	31	28	33	33	8	8	8
10	8	9	9	8	8	12	36	44	45	28	41	34	28	25	35	28	8	9	7
10	8	8	8	8	9	15	36	49	41	33	37	34	28	25	35	17	8	9	8
9	8	8	8	8	9	21	34	46	37	37	35	32	31	28	39	11	8	10	8
9	8	8	9	8	9	27	34	41	33	41	37	30	34	33	35	9	8	9	7
10	8	7	9	8	10	30	36	39	32	43	35	29	30	36	27	8	8	9	8
9	8	8	9	8	11	38	44	43	41	41	35	29	30	36	20	7	7	10	8
9	8	8	9	8	18	38	49	49	45	41	35	32	38	36	14	9	8	9	8
8	8	8	9	9	23	40	42	43	37	43	33	36	42	41	9	8	8	9	8
9	8	7	8	8	16	32	36	33	33	35	33	42	40	35	8	7	8	9	8
9	8	8	8	8	11	19	26	15	25	30	38	36	28	8	7	8	9	7	
9	9	8	9	8	9	9	8	10	7	9	16	24	34	20	8	7	7	9	8
9	8	9	8	8	8	10	8	8	9	8	9	11	18	10	8	7	8	9	7
10	8	8	8	8	8	10	9	8	9	8	8	9	7	7	8	7	8	9	8
10	8	8	8	9	8	9	8	8	9	8	8	10	8	8	9	7	8	9	7
10	8	7	8	8	8	9	9	8	7	8	8	9	8	7	9	7	8	9	8
9	8	9	8	7	8	9	9	7	8	8	8	9	8	8	8	7	8	9	7
9	8	9	9	8	8	10	8	8	8	7	8	9	7	7	7	7	8	9	8

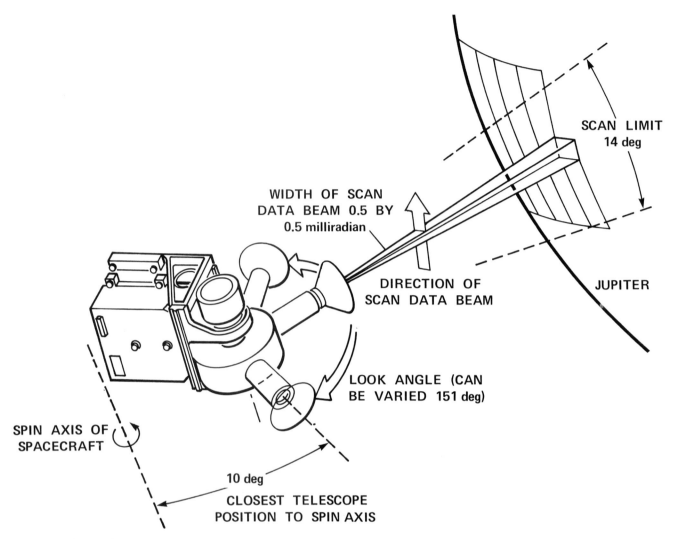

SCAN LIMIT
14 deg

WIDTH OF SCAN
DATA BEAM 0.5 BY
0.5 milliradian

DIRECTION OF
SCAN DATA BEAM

JUPITER

LOOK ANGLE (CAN
BE VARIED 151 deg)

SPIN AXIS OF
SPACECRAFT

10 deg

CLOSEST TELESCOPE
POSITION TO SPIN AXIS

Figure 7-2. Diagram of the imaging photopolarimeter system.

As the spacecraft spins, the line of sight of the telescope sweeps out a large cone in space. This cone intersects Jupiter, and the instrument records the brightness of the reflected light from small contiguous areas of the planet along a swath, as shown in Figure 7-2. The intensity of the red and blue light reflected from each of the scene's elements is translated into a number from 0 to 63, which is telemetered back to Earth. The sequential string of numbers provides information on the different strengths of the red and blue components of each pixel along the swath. On successive rolls of the spacecraft, the swath is displaced sideways step by step, so that, over a period of time, the whole planet is scanned and an image can be built up.

The basic way of displacing the swath is to change the look angle, which is the angle between the telescope's axis and the spin axis of the spacecraft. An automatic feature of the instrument provides for the telescope's look angle to be stepped larger or smaller by a small amount between each roll of the spacecraft, thus giving the required coverage of the whole disc of the planet.

In the example shown in Figure 7-1, the pixel scans are straight, evenly spaced lines, but for the Pioneer pictures the situation is quite different. Basically, the Pioneer scan lines are curved because of the way in which the cone intersects the ellipsoidally shaped planet. Additional distortions

126

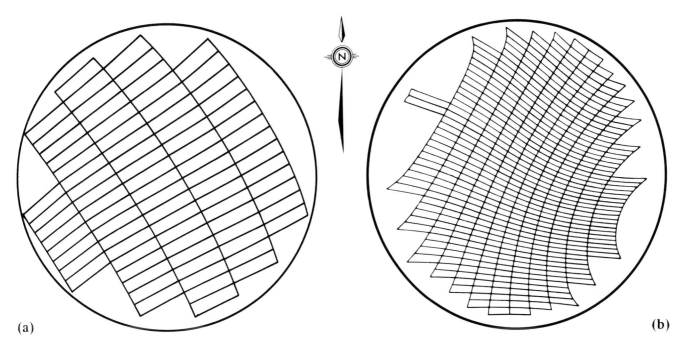

(a)

(b)

Figure 7-3. Two typical scan maps of Jupiter showing how the line of sight of the scan telescope sweeps across Jupiter and builds a picture consisting of discrete areas of different shades of gray. (a) A distant picture produces a relatively undistorted grid. (b) As the spacecraft approaches closer to Jupiter, the trajectory curves more, the spacecraft accelerates, and the imaging photopolarimeter takes longer to scan completely the larger disc of the planet so that more rotation of Jupiter takes place during the scanning process. The result is that the grid is considerably distorted.

occur because the spacecraft moves an appreciable distance along its curved path around the planet during the time it takes to gather all the many swaths of data needed for a complete picture. Also, the planet is spinning about its own axis sufficiently fast to affect the shape of the scan lines.

To reconstruct an image, project scientists need to know precisely where each piece of data came from. For this purpose scan maps are constructed (Figure 7-3). The intersections on the distorted grids shown on these maps are the points that define the small areas from which the light intensities are measured. Only every 25th roll and every 25th sector (group of pixels) are shown on the figure. There would be 625 times as many lines and intersections if all rolls and sectors were shown on the figure.

The imaging photopolarimeter gathers data for only a small part of the complete 360 degree roll; either for 14 or 28 degrees as commanded. The rest of the roll is used to transmit data back to Earth. To tell the instrument at which part of the roll data must be taken, controllers send the spacecraft "spoke" commands. These commands define the part of a roll of the spacecraft in the same way that numbered spokes might define part of the circumference of a wheel.

Many other commands are needed in a complex and carefully thought through sequence to obtain spin-scan images of Jupiter and its major satellites. Figure 7-4 is one of many graphic aids used to formulate and assist the command process. The figure shows how the look angle of the instrument should be changed as a function of time to obtain certain images of the planet and its satellites.

On the figure the three lines of the shaded band labeled Jupiter represent the center and the outer edges of the planet's disc as viewed from the spacecraft. The curved lines labeled JI, JII, etc., show how the look angles of the Galilean satellites change. The two lines labeled SLA1 are positions to which the instrument can be rapidly sent. These are used for setting the instrument to start a sequence of operations and for recovering from an anomalous situation, such as a spurious command. The numbered, irregular line shows the actual position of the telescope as it gathers data over a twenty-four hour period.

Commanding the Imaging Photopolarimeter

The basic command strategy is to take repeated imaging scans of the disc of the planet, interrupted by rapid returns to the starting look angle (SLA) for polarimetry measurements whenever one of Jupiter's Galilean satellites crosses a starting look angle.

For example, starting at the left of Figure 7-4(a), the imaging photopolarimeter is at a starting look angle taking polarimetry on Jupiter's satellite Europa, JII. To get to position 1, 21 commands had been issued, 12 of which were to overcome a problem of unwanted gain changes that had started early in the mission.

Between points 1 and 7 in the sequence, 5 additional gain control commands are sent at 30-minute intervals. At point 7 in the sequence the imaging photopolarimeter is commanded into its threshold mode (Mode 3), where the instrument moves its telescope in small increments continuously until the edge of Jupiter is automatically detected. This point in the sequence involves 17 contiguous commands.

At point 8 in the sequence the instrument is commanded to the imaging mode (Mode 4), and it changes its look angle one step at a time at the imaging rate of 0.5 milliradian per spacecraft revolution. This point in the sequence involves 7 contiguous commands, 4 of which are gain control (sensitivity), and 2 are "spoke" commands.

Point 9 in the sequence involves a single command to reverse the stepping direction of the telescope. Point 10 then involves 17 contiguous commands, 16 of which are gain control commands. The sets of commands at points 9 and 10, consisting of 1 and then 17 commands, are repeated at every similar point in the sequence that follows. Step 14 involves 26 commands, 23 of which are gain control, which places the instrument in the polarimetry mode at starting look angle for the crossing of Jupiter's third Galilean satellite, Ganymede, JIII.

The commanding at point 15 in the sequence is identical to that at point 7, and the commanding at point 16 is identical to that at point 8. At point 19, 3 commands are sent which results in switching back to Mode 3 and stepping beyond SLA1.

The commanding at step 20 reverses the direction of turning movement of the telescope to approach SLA1 from the correct side in order to stop at a position where the third Galilean satellite is observable. It involved 32 contiguous commands.

The rest of the sequence depicted on this chart was constructed by repeating, at the appropriate time, one of the command sequences already described.

Similar sequences were executed for 8 hours a day from 30 days before to 30 days after closest approach, and for 24 hours a day from 8 days before to 8 days after closest approach.

As Pioneer 10 approached closely to Jupiter, the rapid relative motion between the spacecraft and the planet resulted in rapidly changing look angles for the imaging photopolarimeter. Figure 7-4(b) shows a typical observation chart for the time of closest approach. To position the telescope

128

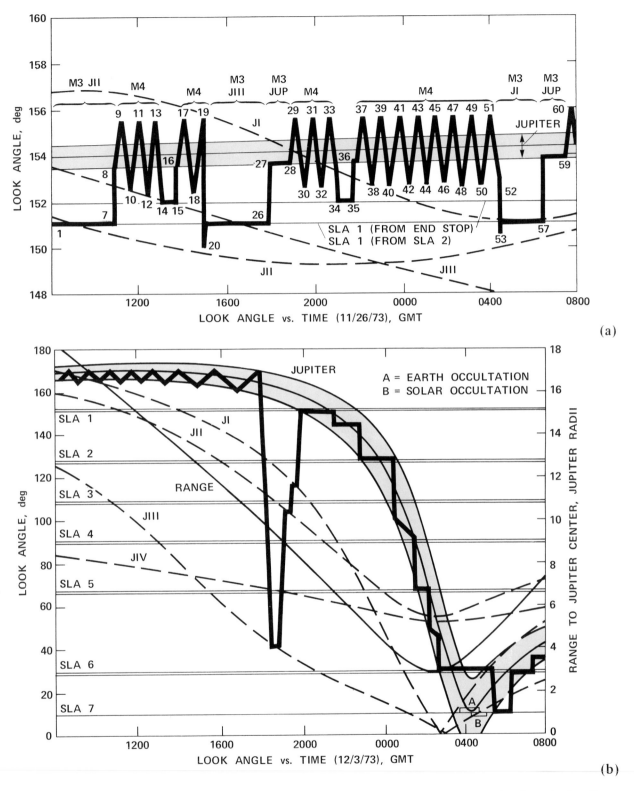

Figure 7-4. Typical 24-hour observation chart used to command the imaging photopolarimeter and later used to determine how the instrument operated at the time pictures were taken. It provides a visual check on what is happening at the spacecraft as far as the look angle of the instrument is concerned. (a) Is how the chart looks when the spacecraft is distant from Jupiter. (b) Shows the chart about the time of closest approach. The main features of the chart are described in the accompanying text.

129

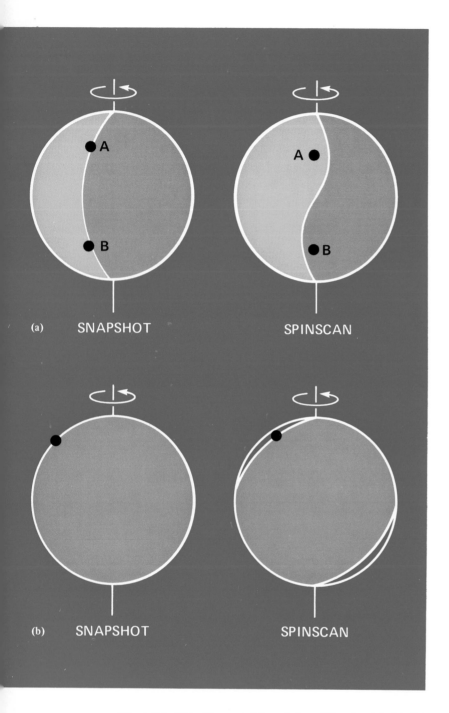

Figure 7-5. Distortion caused by rotation of the planet during the time taken to build up a spin-scan image. (a) Points A and B at the same longitude are scanned at different times, such that A is in darkness when scanned and B is in daylight, though both should be either in darkness or in daylight. Thus the terminator is distorted. (b) Similar effects occur at the limb and the result is that the outline of the disc becomes distorted.

properly, from 14 to 20 contiguous, time-critical commands were required at each point where the telescope look angle curve changes abruptly.

Gathering data for making one of the larger spin-scan images of Jupiter took approximately half an hour. This created a problem since, unlike a normal photograph where all parts of the scene are viewed instantly and from a single point, the Jupiter images were built up from a moving viewpoint of a rotating object. The problem is how to display such an image.

One solution is to reposition the data so that it appears as though the picture was taken at a particular instant in time, for example, the time of the mid-point of the data-taking sequence. This repositioning is done by placing each pixel in a place corresponding to where it was at the chosen "snapshot" time, and not at the place where it was on the planet when it was actually imaged. This process, called geometric rectification, creates a picture that is most nearly like one taken with a camera.

However, there are artifacts arising from this method of display. They are a direct result of the method of picture taking, i.e., the picture is built up over a period of time during which different parts of the object move by different amounts. For example, in Fig. 7-5a points A and B are points with the same longitude on Jupiter. They rotate through the terminator (the shadow edge between night and day) at exactly the same time. A true snapshot, illustrated on the left would show this. However, it could be that with spin-scan imagery point A was imaged a few minutes before sunrise and point B, being imaged later, will be in sunlight. When points A and B are positioned at their correct places in the reconstruction, i.e., at the same longitude, the terminator appears bent as shown — an unreal situation.

A similar problem (Fig. 7-5b) arises at the limb (edge) of the disc. In the spin-scan image, portions of the limb imaged before the equivalent "snapshot" time are displaced in the direction of rotation. There are no data to fill out the correct profile and the shape of the planet is distorted.

These problems are more serious for close-in pictures where it takes longer to scan the disc and where the relative motion effects are more serious.

Figure 7-6(a) shows an image that has been geometrically rectified.

There are other ways to display the data which are less expensive in computing time. One is simply to disregard entirely the geometrical aspects and to display the data exactly as they arrive from the spacecraft. Naturally this results in gross distortion as can be seen from Figure 7-6(b).

Another method is to display the data so as to preserve the correct outline of the planet while accepting some slight distortion of the area within the disc. This effect is appropriately called "rubber sheet" distortion. Small detail in any particular region is accurately portrayed but larger regions may not be spatially related to each other as precisely as in the "snapshot" equivalent picture.

Normally the difference between the two results is small. Figure 7-6(c) shows the same data displayed using this technique. For technical reasons it is easier to preserve the fine detail in the pictures using the correct outline technique, and all the pictures reproduced in the next chapter were made in this way.

(a)

(b)

(c)

Figure 7-6. Three ways to display a spin-scan image of Jupiter: (a) A fully rectified image is almost equivalent to a snapshot — every small area is repositioned to represent a situation of having been taken at the same time as all other areas and from a fixed point in space. But the picture still contains the types of distortions depicted in Figure 7-5. (b) No geometrical corrections are made. The planet shows gross distortion. (c) The correct shape of the planet is obtained, there is a little distortion of the individual features, but this third display mode requires only a relatively small amount of computer processing compared with the more complicated processing required for display (a).

131

Apart from difficulties in presenting the pictures with the correct geometry, there are other factors that determine the quality of the image. For example, there were occasional data dropouts — loss of data — that resulted in losing parts of pictures. Such losses ranged from a small section of one line of data, caused by a missing telemetry data frame, to the loss of one or more continuous lines. Replacing the missing parts with black fill, or simply skipping over the dropped lines, results in pictures with distracting features which, for scientific and esthetic reasons, it is desirable to reduce or to eliminate. This can be done by interpolating average values for the missing data from surrounding good data. Such "cosmetic" enhancement can be satisfactorily applied only when the fraction of mission data is small. Figure 7-7 shows a severe case before and after treatment with "cosmetic" enhancement.

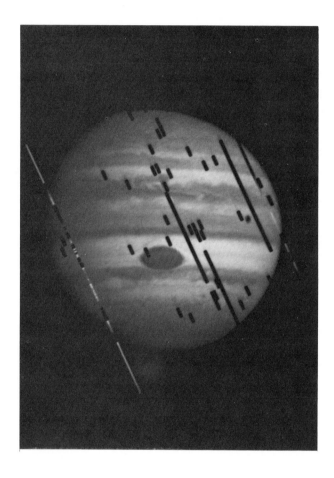 

Figure 7-7. Before and after correction of dropped frames of data from a spin-scan image. This cosmetic enhancement is achieved by computer processing to smooth over and insert areas of missing data.

During the acquisition of some images the sensitivity of the imaging photopolarimeter would change, sometimes deliberately as a result of a command and sometimes as a result of a malfunction due to radiation. The effect of this is to darken, or lighten, bands within the picture. Compensating for these sensitivity changes is straightforward, and Figure 7-8 shows the before and after images.

There was another minor problem with some of the Pioneer 10 imaging data. The blue picture was everywhere too bright by a fixed amount. This fault was corrected in the data processing.

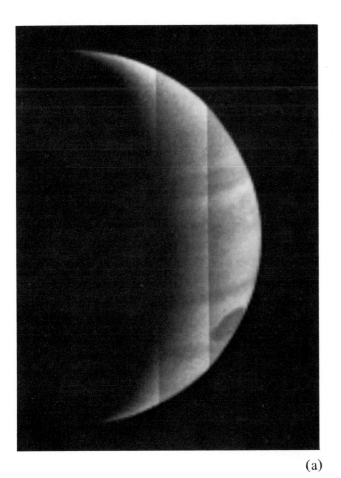

(a)

(b)

Figure 7-8. Before and after correction of sensitivity (gain) changes. The sensitivity of the imaging photopolarimeter was changed to compensate for changing brightness of the planet as the instrument scanned different areas of the disc. This resulted in the banding on the spin-scan image (a). Computer processing corrected the banding to produce the image (b).

Two other problems occurred with the imaging data provided by Pioneer 10. Figure 7-9 shows a fine, ripple-like structure of low contrast covering parts of the red image. It represents noise of unknown origin, and, because of its partially random nature, it is difficult to eliminate from the images. This figure shows a particularly noticeable example, although the effect can also be seen in several of the pictures in the next chapter. The other defect, which also occurred in some Pioneer 11 images, is illustrated in Fig. 7-10. The apparent flattening of portions of the limb of Jupiter is caused by a characteristic of the mechanism that changes the look angle of the telescope.

Figure 7-9. Noise of unknown origin affects the red channel image to produce a ripple-like effect which is difficult to correct because of its semi-random nature.

Figure 7-10. A slight flattening of the limb in places is caused by a characteristic of the imaging photopolarimeter instrument's design that results in a slightly non-uniform stepping across the planet.

Figure 7-11. A raw data dump (i.e., unprocessed picture) from Pioneer 11. On the right is an image that has been severely distorted by a fault in the telescope drive system. The image on the left suffers from a few dropped frames.

The intense radiation problems affected the IPP on Pioneer 11 somewhat differently. After its passage through the most intense part of the radiation belts, the telescope drive mechanism became quite erratic. Instead of stepping uniformly across the planet, it would skip backwards and forwards in a seemingly quite random manner, sometimes not moving at all for several rolls of the spacecraft. The effect of this was to create severely-distorted images. Figure 7-11 shows an example of this problem. Special computer programs will have to be written before these data can be correctly assembled into pictures. The figure shows a raw data dump of blue-channel data for images D17 and D18. Image D17 is normal except for a few dropped frames whereas D18, on the right, suffers from this stepping fault. The tick marks around the edge of the picture are used for identifying the roll and sector numbers of the various features in the data.

The imaging photopolarimeter gathered data using the red and blue components of the light reflected from Jupiter. To make color pictures it is necessary to have three colored components, such as red, green, and blue. Reconstructing with red and blue only would give rise to a severely purple-tinted image. Scientists were able to make three color composite images by synthesizing a green image. This green image was derived from information contained in the red and blue channels and from knowledge of the color balance and color content of Jupiter images as obtained from ground-based observations. The method works well for Jupiter since the planet has no significant green or purple coloration; a photograph of Jupiter taken through a green filter closely resembles a composite of photographs taken through red and blue filters. Figure 7-12 shows the real red and blue components, the synthetic green, and the color composite formed by the photographic superposition of these three. The effect of not including a synthetic green channel is also shown.

This use of color synthesis often assists scientists in their interpretation of clouds and features; however, too much emphasis should not be given to the exact hues and saturations of colors in the Jupiter pictures from Pioneer, because only two of the three components are real. This is even more applicable in the case of the satellites imaged by the Pioneers. Since Earth-based observations have not resolved color features on these satellites, there is no standard for comparison of the colors.

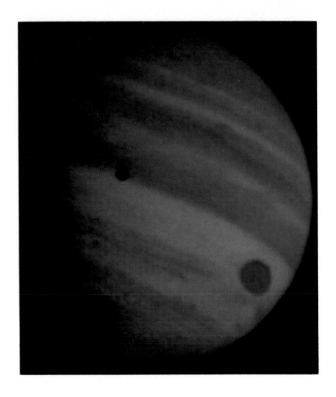

Figure 7-12. Constructing a colored picture of Jupiter from the red and blue data channels requires construction of a green image first, to combine with the red and blue. This produces a lifelike image on which the color balance has been adjusted to correspond with the best Earth-based observations of Jupiter. Without the green picture an objectionable purplish Jupiter would result from mixing the blue and red images alone.

8
Encounter with the Giant

DURING THE MONTHS of November and December of 1973, Pioneer 10 sent back over 500 images of Jupiter. Most of these were taken from a comparatively large distance from the planet and show very little detail compared to pictures that have already been taken with telescopes based on Earth. However, those pictures that were obtained within 48 hours of the closest approach of the spacecraft to Jupiter are considerably better than any seen previously. Not only is the resolution greater, thereby revealing hitherto unseen details on the planet, but Jupiter has now been seen from viewpoints not available to observers based on Earth.

Because Jupiter is many times further from the Sun than the Earth, the angle subtended by the Earth and the Sun at Jupiter, i.e., the phase angle, never exceeds 11.5 degrees. Astronomers can see the planet only as a fully illuminated disc. From Earth, it is not possible to see Jupiter illuminated from the side or from behind as the Moon can be seen, with its crescent and half-moon shapes. Pioneer 10 provided the first opportunity to view Jupiter under varying illumination conditions, and this chapter presents some of the images obtained.

Figure 8-1 shows the trajectory of the spacecraft for 20 hours before and after its closest approach to Jupiter. As it approached the planet, the spacecraft was below the equatorial plane. Later it

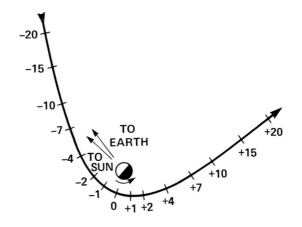

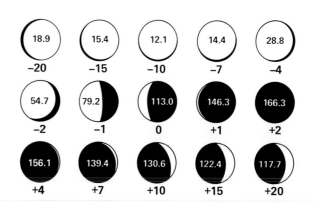

Figure 8-1. Phases of Jupiter as seen by the spacecraft from 20 hours before to 20 hours after closest approach.

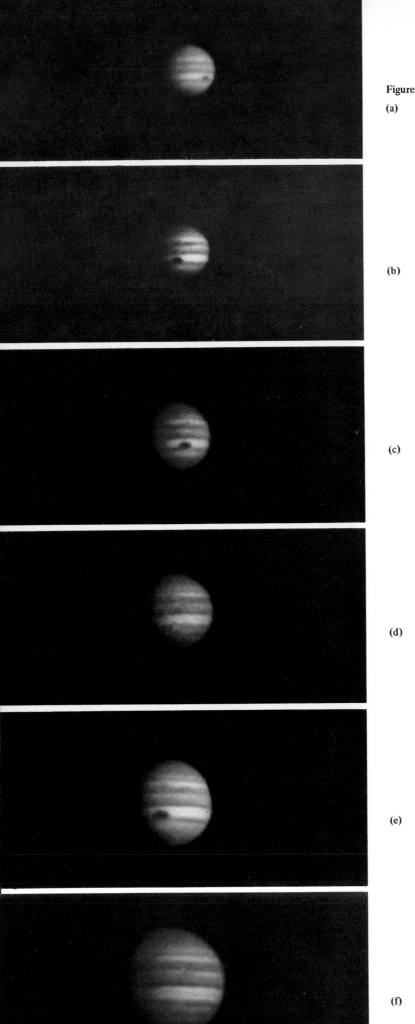

Figure 8-2

(a)

(b)

(c)

(d)

(e)

(f)

crossed this plane and departed from the planet north of the plane. The lower part of the illustration shows schematically the change in the illumination of the disc of Jupiter, as seen from the spacecraft, at times corresponding to the positions of the spacecraft shown on the trajectory.

At 20 hours before closest approach, the dark limb is at the left of the planet. At 12 hours, it is under the planet as the spacecraft approaches below the equatorial plane. Just before closest approach, the dark limb slips around to the right side of the planet. Then the terminator rapidly sweeps across the view of the planet from the spacecraft, until the whole disc is dark as the spacecraft plunges into the planet's shadow. As Pioneer 10 emerges from the shadow, its images reveal a crescent Jupiter, the beginning of a unique series of pictures.

In the following pages, the images taken within four days of closest approach are designated with a code, such as A28 or B17. "A" images are before closest approach (periapsis) and "B" images are after closest approach. A fuller explanation of the code and a listing of the significant information about each image is given in Appendix 2. All dates and times used in this chapter are Universal Time (UT) which is the same as Greenwich Mean Time (GMT). DOY stands for day of year, i.e., January 1 is DOY 1, and December 31 is DOY 365.

The series of blue-channel pictures on this and the facing page was taken at two-day intervals, starting on DOY 321, 17 days before Pioneer 10's closest approach to Jupiter. None of these pictures has resolution as good as that which can be obtained from Earth. The scan lines, because they are so few, are quite evident.

The Great Red Spot and the banded structure are clearly visible even at these great distances, which range from 16 to 7.5 million km (10 to 4.7 million mi.). The terminator is on the west side of the disc of the planet and displaced slightly toward the south.

It is interesting to note that the detail, as seen by the IPP, is approximately the same as that which would be seen by the unaided human eye at

140

Figure 8-3

the same distance from Jupiter. All the pictures reproduced in this chapter show Jupiter as it might have been seen by an astronaut in a manned spacecraft, flying by Jupiter along the path of Pioneer 10.

The pictures on this and the facing page have all been reproduced to the same angular scale. The relative sizes are exactly as they would have appeared to an observer on the spacecraft as it approached Jupiter. These blue channel images have been selected to show Jupiter at approximately one day intervals, starting six days before periapsis. The last image shown in this series has a resolution comparable with that obtainable from Earth when the "seeing" conditions are good. Many of the pictures obtained over this period of time show satellites in the field of view. They are, however, too far away from the spacecraft to be resolved into detail and usually too far from the planet's disc to be seen in the pictures shown here. One satellite appears in the last frame of this series, slightly below and to the left of the disc of the planet.

(b)

Figure	Mid time DOY:hr:min	Distance 10^6 km	10^6 mi.	Phase angle degrees
8-2(a)	321:01:36	16.0	10.0	37.3
8-2(b)	323:02:04	14.3	8.9	37.2
8-2(c)	325:04:07	12.6	7.8	37.0
8-2(d)	327:01:53	11.0	6.8	36.7
8-2(e)	329:06:46	9.1	5.7	36.1
8-2(f)	331:04:30	7.5	4.7	35.3

(c)

Figure	Mid time DOY:hr:min	Distance 10^6 km	10^6 mi.	Phase angle degrees
8-3(a)	332:16:02	6.2	3.9	34.9
8-3(b)	333:01:44	5.8	3.6	34.4
8-3(c)	334:07:03	4.6	2.9	32.6
8-3(d)	335:12:53	3.4	2.1	30.0

(d)

Figure 8-4

(a)

This spectacular series of consecutive pictures was taken over a period of four hours, between 44-1/2 and 40-1/2 hours before periapsis. The Great Red Spot is prominent, and the shadow of Io traverses the disc of the planet. Cosmetic enhancement as described in Chapter 7 was applied to all these images, especially to A49. A49 is shown before and after cosmetic enhancement in Figure 7-7.

(b)

(c)

Figure	Image no.	Mid time DOY:hr:min	Range 10^5 km	10^5 mi.	Phase angle degrees
8-4(a)	A51	336:06:55	25.8	16.0	27.3
8-4(b)	A50	336:07:31	25.6	15.9	27.2
8-4(c)	A49	336:08:11	25.3	15.7	27.0
8-4(d)	A48	336:08:48	25.0	15.5	26.9
8-4(e)	A47	336:09:30	24.7	15.4	26.7
8-4(f)	A46	336:10:07	24.4	15.2	26.6

142

The series of pictures, A39, A35, A31, and A28, on the next four pages shows one complete rotation of the planet. The final picture in the series is the last picture possible before the planet overfilled the field of view. Part of the data used to create A35 is missing. This results in the comb-like truncation of the northwest limb. This same effect occurs in several pictures in this chapter.

The gross morphology of belts and zones, with structures showing turbulence and convective cells in the middle latitudes of the planet, is clearly seen. The small white spots surrounded by dark rings, seen mainly in the southern hemisphere, indicate regions of intense vertical convective activity, somewhat similar to cumulonimbus or thunderclouds.

In places where the clouds are relatively featureless and have a bluish coloration, the IPP image provides a look down into the deepest and warmest parts of the atmosphere. These are called "blue festoons."

(d)

(e)

(f)

Figure	Image no.	Mid time DOY:hr:min	Range 10^5 km	10^5 mi.	Phase angle degrees
8-5(a)	A39	336:14:33	22.3	13.8	25.5
8-5(b)	A35	336:17:21	20.9	13.0	24.7
8-5(c)	A31	336:20:18	19.5	12.1	23.8
8-5(d)	A28	336:22:31	18.4	11.4	23.0

143

Figure 8-5 (a)

144

Figure 8-5 (b)

145

Figure 8-5 (c)

146

Figure 8-5 (d)

147

At the head of this bright plume is a rising column of warm particles from a source deep within the clouds. The tail is to the left because the atmosphere moves more slowly at the upper regions than lower down. The southerly deflection of the plume, and the scalloped edges of the belt above the plume, support the theory that there is strong convective circulation between the lower and middle latitude belts and zones.

A color picture is shown together with the black and white images of the blue and red channels from which the colored image was constructed.

Figure	Image no.	Mid time DOY:hr:min	Range 10^5 km	10^5 mi.	Phase angle degrees
8-6	A22	337:08:52	13.0	8.1	17.8

Figure 8-6 (a)

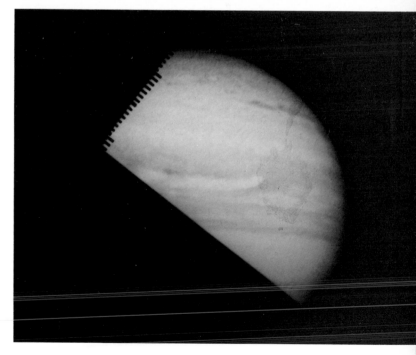

(b) Blue channel

(c) Red channel

Red spots, other than the Great Red Spot, have been observed from the ground on previous occasions. This first close look at a northern hemisphere red spot shows convincingly the great morphological similarity between it and the well-known and much studied Great Red Spot in the southern hemisphere. Ground-based observations indicate that this particular feature is very young — probably not more than 18-months old at the time of the passage of Pioneer 10.

Figure	Image no.	Mid time DOY:hr:min	Range 10^5 km	10^5 mi.	Phase angle degrees
8-7	A-16	337:11:23	11.5	7.2	16.0

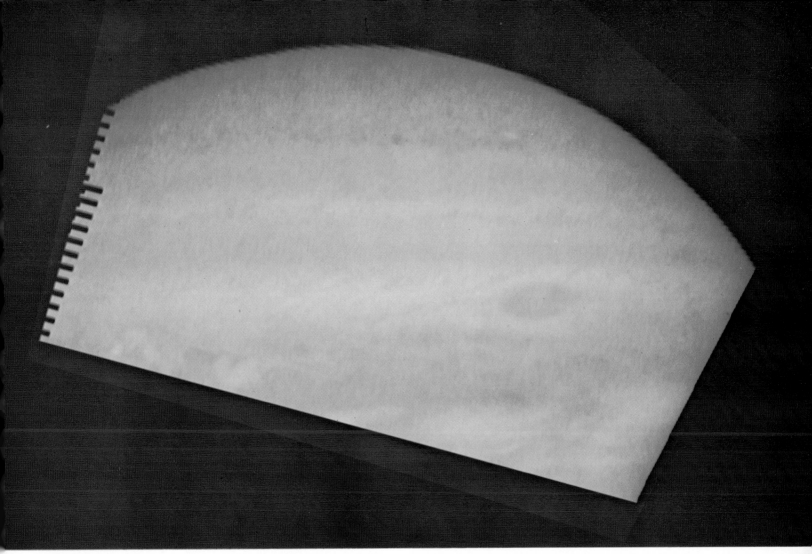

Figure 8-7 (a)

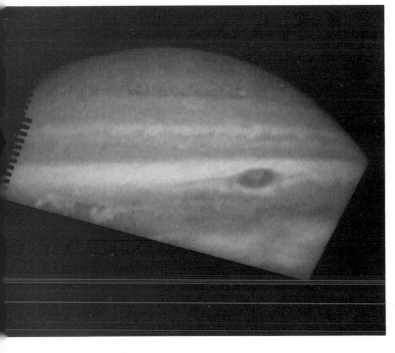

(b) Blue channel

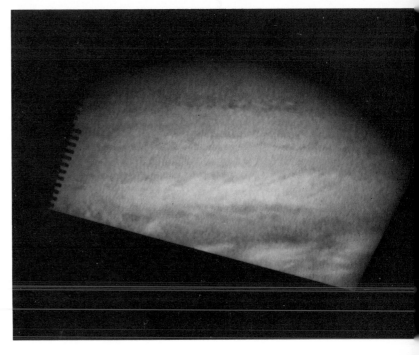

(c) Red channel

Figure 8-8 (a)

(b) Blue channel

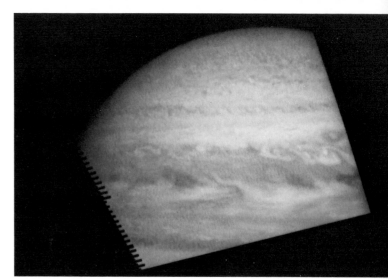

(c) Red channel

The pictures on this and the facing page are of similar areas of Jupiter and provide the best coverage of this enormously turbulent region. The "hooks" are several thousands of kilometers in extent. The belt structure is unstable at higher latitudes. At the top of the pictures, a belt fragment, the darker elongated feature, can be seen in the transition zone between the belts and the relatively smooth looking polar region.

152

Figure 8-9 (a)

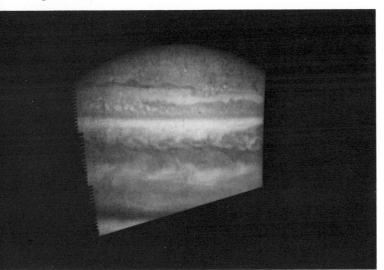

(b) Blue channel

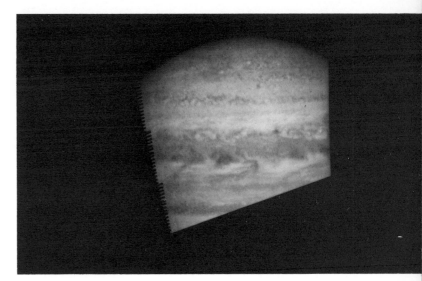

(c) Red channel

Figure	Image no.	Mid time DOY:hr:min	Range 10^4 km	10^4 mi.	Phase angle degrees
8-8	A9	337:14:47	95.4	59.4	13.4
8-9	A8	337:15:17	92.4	57.4	13.1

153

Figure 8-10 (a)

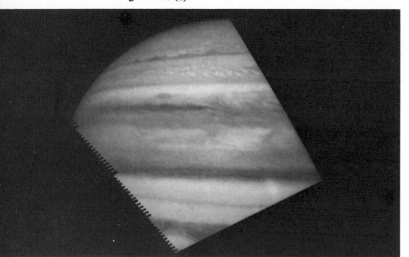

(b) Blue channel

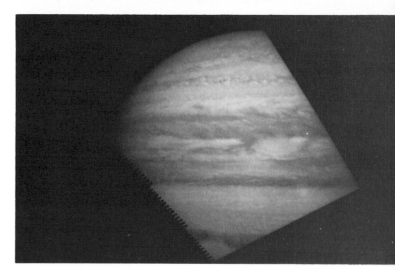

(c) Red channel

On this and the facing page is shown the type of fine detail revealed in the cloud photographs that will help scientists to unravel the complex behavior of the Jovian atmosphere.

In all the images, gross differences between the red and blue images are apparent. The fine repetitive wave-like structure discernible in the red channel image, which shows up as a bluish ripple on the colored image, is not real and should be ignored.

154

Figure 8-11 (a)

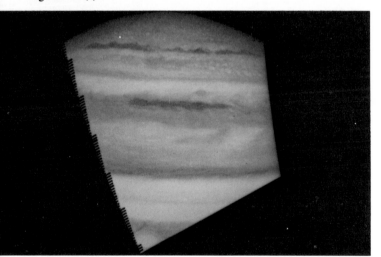

(b) Blue channel

(c) Red channel

Figure	Image no.	Mid time DOY:hr:min	Range 10^4 km	10^4 mi.	Phase angle degrees
8-10	A7	337:16:19	86.1	53.6	12.4
8-11	A6	337:17:05	81.4	50.6	12.2

155

Figure 8-12 (a)

The differences between the red and blue channel images are not only intriguing, but also important from the scientific analysis standpoint. This image shows again the plume conspicuous on Figure 8-6. But the detail is very much improved on this picture, which is one of the best close encounter pictures. Here features are seen that can be only glimpsed from Earth. Unfortunately, Pioneer 10 flew by so quickly that movements in the clouds cannot be detected between one picture and another. Even so, the nature of the detail enables inferences to be drawn concerning the dynamic properties of the Jovian atmosphere from these images.

Figure	Image no.	Mid time DOY:hr:min	Range 10^4 km	10^4 mi.	Phase angle degrees
8-12	A5	337:18:28	72.6	45.1	12.2

(b) Blue channel

157

(c) Red channel

Figure 8-13

(a)

(b)

While receding from Jupiter, Pioneer 10 showed Jupiter from a viewpoint never before seen by man: sunrise on a crescent-shaped planet. This series of images shows the northern hemisphere red spot, the Great Red Spot, and parts of the large plume. Contrast is lower in this crescent phase — a fact that can be explained in terms of the way in which the cloud particles scatter light. Irregularities in the profile of Jupiter are caused by a characteristic of the mechanism that drives the telescope.

The final picture in this series is the last one taken by the Pioneer 10 spacecraft on its epic journey, on New Year's Eve 1973.

158

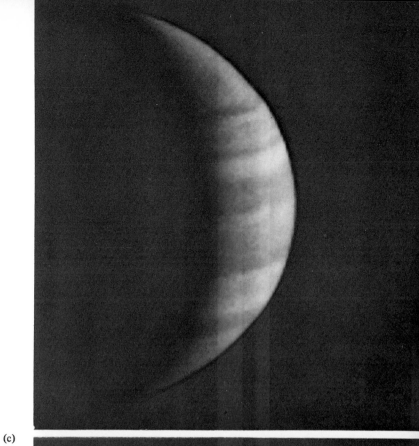

(c)

(d)

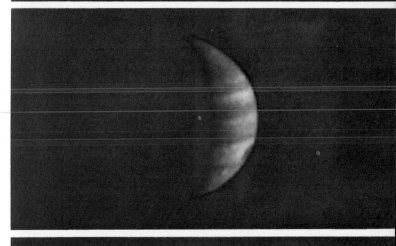

(e)

Figure	Image no.	Mid time DOY:hr:min	Range		Phase angle degrees
			10^5 km	10^5 mi.	
8-13(a)	B11	339:00:50	14.7	9.1	116.4
8-13(b)	B17	339:04:54	16.8	10.5	114.0
8-13(c)	B23	339:08:09	18.5	11.5	112.4
8-13(d)	B39	339:21:25	24.9	15.5	108.2
8-13(e)	B69	341:17:08	43.7	27.2	102.5
8-13(f)	— —	365:18:08	160.0	99.5	97.0

159

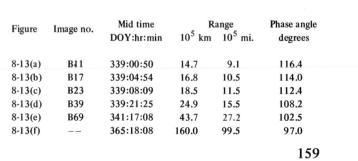

(f)

9
The Giant Revisited

Pioneer 11, the second spacecraft to fly by Jupiter, returned approximately 460 images of Jupiter and its Galilean satellites during the period 18 November to 9 December 1974. As explained in earlier chapters the trajectory of Pioneer 11 past Jupiter was quite different from that of Pioneer 10. Not only did Pioneer 11 approach much closer to Jupiter's surface — to 0.60 Jovian radii compared with 1.82 Jovian radii for Pioneer 10, but also the spacecraft approached from south of the equator and left from above (to the north). This approach allowed the spacecraft to obtain many unprecedented images of the high latitude, near polar regions. And because the outgoing leg was highly inclined to the equator of Jupiter, several good images were obtained of the planet's north pole.

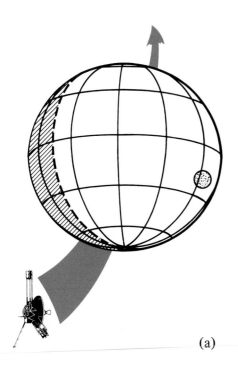

(a)

(b)

Figure 9-1. View of Jupiter from the spacecraft for the incoming (a) and outgoing (b) path.

161

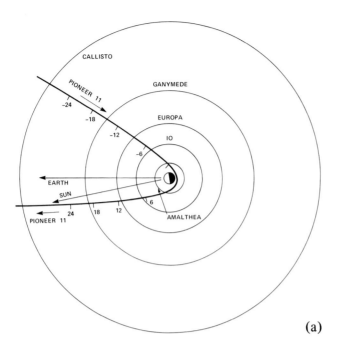

(a)

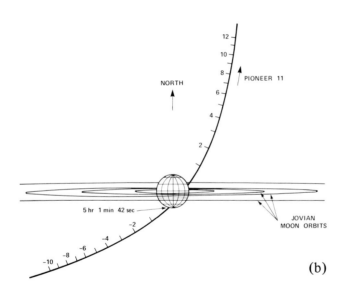

(b)

Figure 9-2. The path of Pioneer 11 past Jupiter shown (a) from above the north pole of the planet, and (b) as seen from the equatorial plane.

To distinguish these Pioneer 11 images from those of Pioneer 10, a "C" and "D" notation is used with the image numbers being sequential in time starting at periapsis. "C" images were obtained before periapsis, "D" images after. Full details of these images are given in Appendix 2.

On the facing page the two images taken about a day before and after encounter show the attitude of Jupiter during approach and departure. Unlike Pioneer 10, no rapidly changing terminator position is seen. In all "C" images the terminator is in a position similar to that seen in C22 and all "D" images have the terminator in a position similar to that seen in D17.

The closeness of the approach, and the high relative velocity of the spacecraft over the surface meant that very close-in images could not be obtained; the data would have been gathered too sparsely for later reconstructing into an image. Four pictures on each side of closest approach (C4 through D4) were taken in the step inhibit mode of operation, in which the spacecraft motion alone provided the sweep to build up the picture. Four of this series are shown later in Figs. 9-11 through 9-14. At this close range only partial views of the planet could be obtained.

At about one day before periapsis, a malfunction affected the stepping function of the telescope and a few images were partially lost before a work-around could be effected. Images C16–C10 were affected in this manner. Following this radiation damage the University of Arizona observing team worked for many days and nights to make the necessary corrections to the command sequences to ensure that no more images would be lost.

Figures 9-3 and 9-4. Typical views of Jupiter as Pioneer 11 approached (top) and departed from (bottom) the planet. Figure 9-3 (Image C22) was taken 33 hours before periapsis at a distance of 2,142,000 km (1,331,000 mi.). Figure 9-4 (Image D17) was taken 32 hours after periapsis at a distance of 2,085,000 km (1,296,000 mi.).

Figure 9-5. Image C9. Range 1,235,000 km (767,000 mi.) at
16 hours before periapsis.

164

Figure 9-6. Image C8. Range 1,144,000 km (711,000 mi.) about
14 hours before periapsis. This is one of the better pictures of
the Great Red Spot. See also Figure 9-11 for a closer view.

Figure 9-7. Image C7. Range 1,038,000 km (645,000 mi.) about
13 hours before encounter.

166

Figure 9-8. Image C6. Almost two hours after Figure 9-7, this image was taken at 936,000 km (582,000 mi.). Great detail is now apparent in the belts and zones including many light and dark cells indicating convective activity in the south temperate zones. Also a small red spot is revealed in the northern hemisphere.

167

Figure 9-9. Image C5. Range 765,000 km (475,000 mi.) at 8 hours
   before periapsis.

168

Figure 9-10. The picture is shown here exactly as it was received at the Ames Research Center. No computer processing of any kind has yet been performed. This figure should be compared with Figure 9-9 (opposite) of which it is the blue channel data. The red channel problems were essentially identical. In producing Figure 9-9 four computer corrections were applied. First, the shape of the planet, distorted by the spacecraft's motion and viewing geometry was corrected. Second, the three bands of varying image intensity, a consequence of maximizing the scientific value of the data for photometric analysis of the clouds, were eliminated. Third, the black areas of missing data caused by problems at the receiving station, were filled in by interpolation between neighboring values (see Chapter 7). Fourth, two rolls of unsynchronized spacecraft data, showing as diagonal streaks, were correctly repositioned.

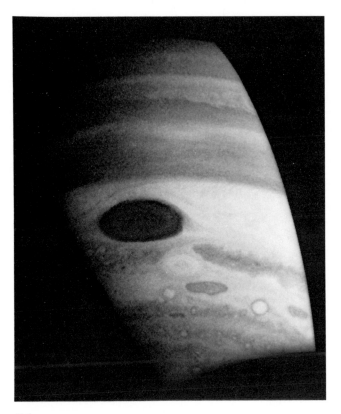

(b)

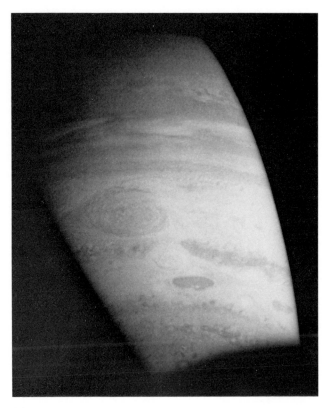

(c)

Figure 9-11. Close up of Jupiter's Great Red Spot (Image C3).
Obtaining this image of the Great Red Spot of Jupiter was one of Pioneer 11's most exciting prospects for planetary astronomers. The highest resolution image of the spot obtained by Pioneer 10 had been spoiled by radiation problems, but Pioneer 11 was successful in obtaining the unique image on the facing page (Figure 9-11a). The area covered on the planet is shown as the inset below the photograph.

This is the best view so far of the Great Red Spot of Jupiter. It was obtained at a range of 545,000 km (320,000 mi.) above the cloud tops.

The image contains more than 4000 individual pixels (see Chapter 7) of measurable data in the red area of the spot thereby providing a wealth of detail of the markings since each pixel represents an area of approximately 237 km (147 mi.) square.

Planetary scientists are deriving new interpretations of the Red Spot from this unique image. Despite the relatively high resolution obtained there is much less fine structure visible in the spot than in comparable images at other latitudes, for example, in Figures 9-12 and 9-14. The Red Spot appears to lie in the most quiescent zone of the planet, which may contribute to its stability.

There is very little internal detail in the blue image (Figure 9-11b), the main feature being the dark border encircling the periphery. A break in this border seems to exist in the northeast part of the spot, where some intermixing of the red material into the South Tropical Zone appears to be taking place.

Much internal detail is revealed in the red image (Figure 9-11c), but perhaps most significant are two circular outlines which cross over near the center of the spot. This same feature

was also seen in Pioneer 10 images. No clear suggestion of motions within the spot is evident from this image. The image does not show direct evidence of flow lines from any single region inside the spot which might be interpreted as a source or a sink of the red material.

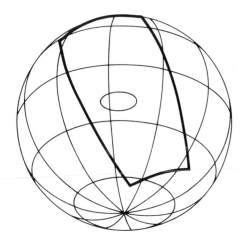

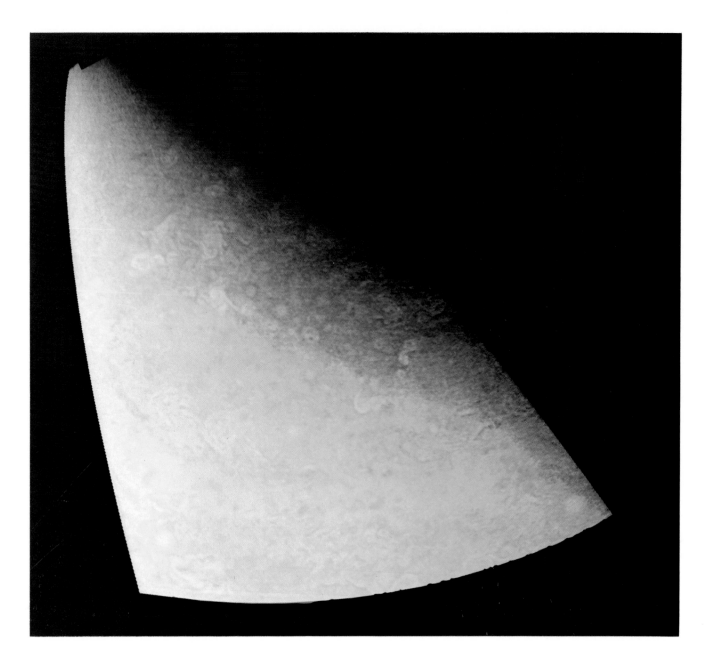

Figure 9-12. The first image (D1) taken 3½ hours after periapsis at a range of 375,000 km (233,000 mi.) shows the first view of the north pole of Jupiter. There is still great activity in the cloud forms at high latitudes, but the banded structure of the tropics changes to a random pattern of cells and turbulence down to the limits of resolution.

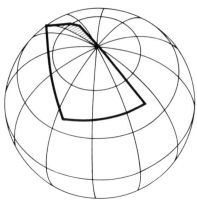

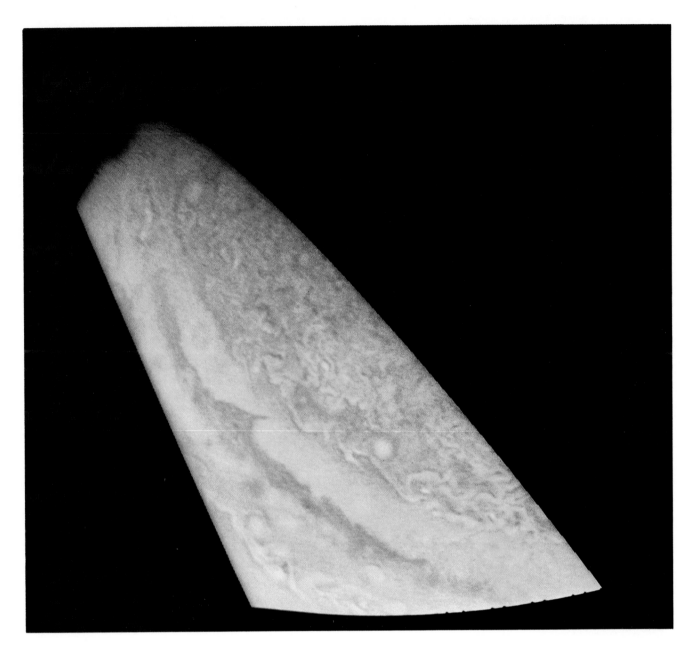

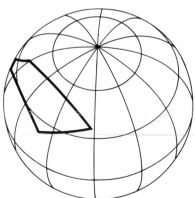

Figure 9-13. This image (D2) would have been contiguous with Figure 9-12 but for a reconfiguration of the instrument to guard against radiation problems. This image is further from the pole as shown in the inset. The time was 4 hours after periapsis, and the distance 435,000 km (270,000 mi.).

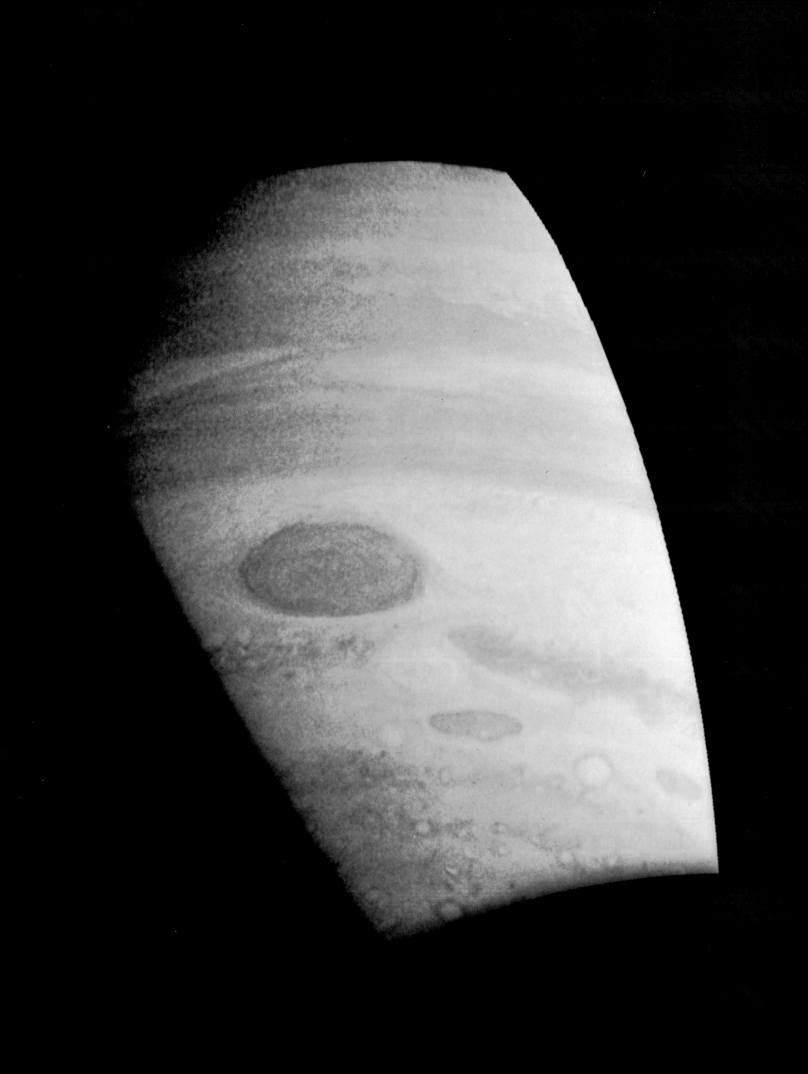

(b)

(c)

Figure 9-14. This image (D4) is perhaps the most scientifically important image of Jupiter obtained by Pioneer 11. It covers an area of the planet from the equator to the north polar regions and provides details of the range of cloud features from bands to polar cells. Figure 9-14a (opposite) is the computer processed image. The colors are, however, probably less authentic than those of the images before periapsis because of an apparent change in the behavior of the instrument after passage through the intense radiation belts. Figure 9-14(b) and (c) above show smaller versions of the blue and red channel images, respectively. The comparatively large uniform area on the red-channel image is caused by detector saturation which resulted in loss of information. This was a result of having deliberately set the gain at a high level so that the darker regions near the north pole would be well imaged. The corresponding area in the colored image also lacks this information, which further affects the color balance. The range for this image was 610,000 km (379,000 mi.).

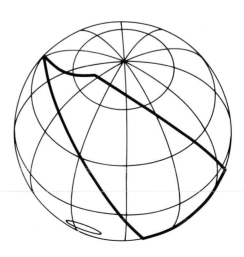

175

Figure 9-15. Image D8. Range 1,079,000 km (671,000 mi.), 13½ hours after periapsis.

The series of images Figures 9-15 through 9-20 shows Jupiter receding as Pioneer 11 leaves the giant planet and rises high above the ecliptic plane on its way to Saturn. Due to an anomaly which affected the rate at which the telescope swept across the planet the command sequence to obtain these pictures had to be changed day by day. Nevertheless all were obtained without any being lost, despite the fact that there was no time to verify the command sequence by computer simulations in advance.

Figure 9-16. Image D10. Range 1,310,000 km (814,000 mi.),
17½ hours after periapsis.

Figure 9-17. Image D11. Range 1,539,000 km (956,000 mi.),
21½ hours after periapsis.

Figure 9-18. Image D12. Range 1,586,000 km (985,000 mi.), at
22 hours after periapsis.

Figure 9-19. Image D14. Range 1,777,000 km (1,104,000 mi.), at
26 hours after periapsis.

Figure 9-20. Image D15. Range 1,847,000 km (1,148,000 mi.), at
27 hours after periapsis.

178

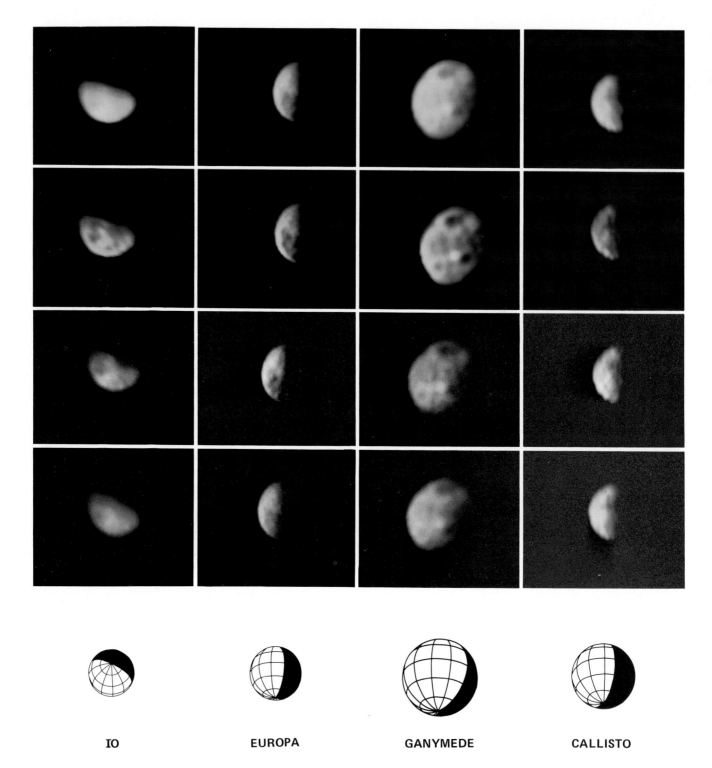

| IO | EUROPA | GANYMEDE | CALLISTO |

Figure 9-21. The best images of the four Galilean satellites obtained
by the two Pioneer spacecraft are shown here. Each column is
for an individual satellite. The top image is the color composite,
the next image shows this same color image as enhanced further
by computer processing. Below this are shown the blue channel
image followed by the red channel image. Finally, at the bottom
of each column is a line drawing to identify the viewing aspect.

180

With telescopes on the Earth, astronomers are afforded only the barest hints of what kind of markings appear on the Galilean satellites. Pioneers 10 and 11 recorded images of all four of these satellites which provide a much better idea of the albedo and color variations across the discs. Although all colors may not be represented properly since only red and blue data were recorded, it is certain that the yellow-orange regions are redder than white regions.

Only one good image of Io has been obtained. This is from Pioneer 11. The Pioneer 10 image of Io was missed completely due to the radiation environment of Jupiter. The Pioneer 11 image is a view from over the north pole of Io. From the Earth there have been observations suggesting that the polar regions of Io are reddish colored. On this Pioneer image there is orange coloration at the polar region, as contrasted with the whitish equatorial part of the satellite. Io is strongly affected by the radiation environment of Jupiter since its orbit is well within the radiation belts and the satellite sweeps up energetic particles from these belts. Also, its orbital motion affects the decametric radio emission of Jupiter. Although there is no

indication of it in this picture, Io is the only Galilean satellite which is known to have an atmosphere although it is much less dense than that of the Earth or even that of Mars.

The single image of Europa recorded by Pioneer 10 has little color variation, but there is a broad dark region with some gross detail. Europa is among the brightest of satellites and is thought to have a crust of mainly water ice.

Two excellent images of Ganymede were recorded by the Pioneer spacecraft. These images show little color variation, but substantial albedo differences over the disc of this largest of the satellites. Ganymede's low density may be due to the presence of a high percentage of ices with some silicates from primordial material and from impacting material from space.

Several good images of Callisto show only small color differences and small albedo variations. The darkest of the Galilean satellites, Callisto has a low density which requires a high percentage of ices in its bulk structure. Two different views — one a half-moon shape (reproduced here) and the other a gibbous shape — show the same prominent light region close to the terminator.

| Satellite | | Image | Midtime | Range | Pixel size | Phase angle | Sub S/C, deg | |
No.	Name	number	Year DOY hr min	km	km	deg	Lat.	LCM
JI	Io	D7	(1974) 337:17: 33	756,000	376	67	+60	184
JII	Europa	A4	(1973) 337:19: 24	324,000	161	87	−24	290
JIII	Ganymede	C5½	(1974) 336:19: 38	739,000	367	44	−29	46
JIV	Callisto	C12	(1974) 336:09: 37	787,000	391	82	−34	33

Note: DOY: day of year
LCM: longitude of central meridian

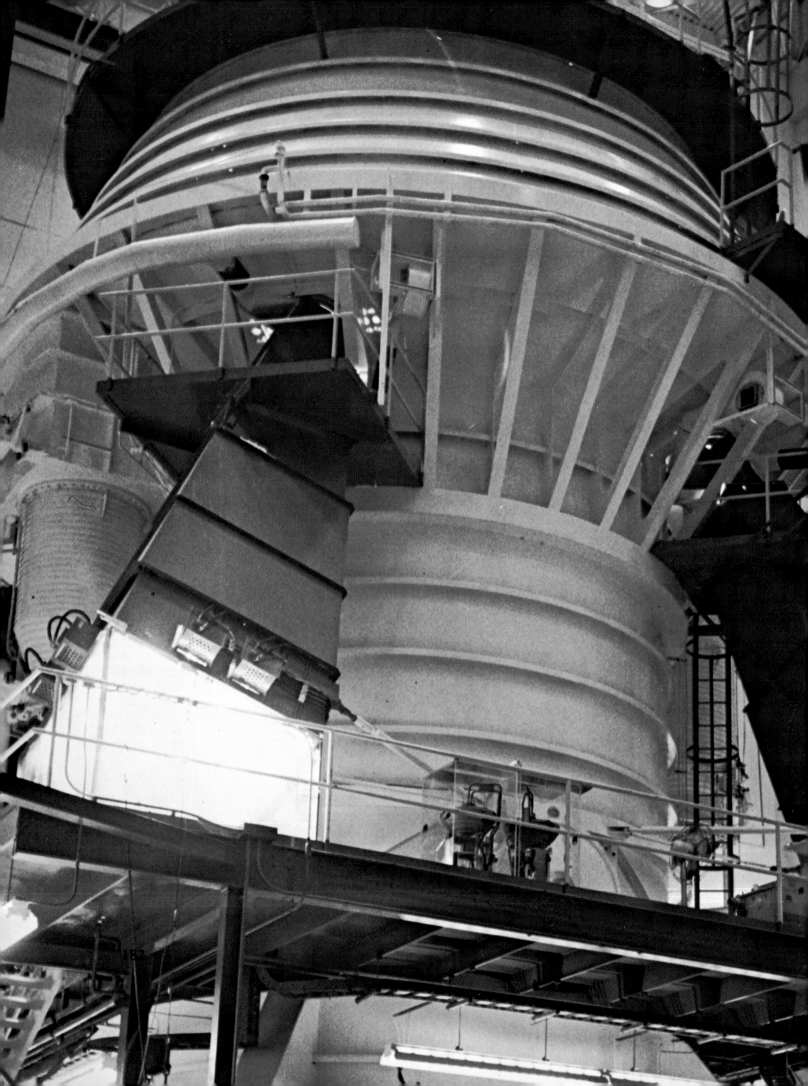

Epilog
Interstellar Cave Painting

IN A HIGH VACUUM Pioneer 10 gleamed under the harsh lights of an artificial Sun in the space simulator at TRW Systems, California, its final tests underway prior to shipment to Kennedy Space Center. A group of science correspondents from the national press were at TRW Systems for a briefing on Pioneer and had been invited to see the spacecraft under test.

Looking at Pioneer through the portholes of the simulator, one of the correspondents, Eric Burgess, then with *The Christian Science Monitor,* visualized the passage of Pioneer 10 beyond the Solar System as mankind's first emissary to the stars. This spacecraft should carry a special message from mankind, he thought, a message that would tell any finder of the spacecraft a million or even a billion years hence that planet Earth had evolved an intelligent species that could think beyond its own time and beyond its own Solar System.

He mentioned this to Richard Hoagland, a freelance writer, and Don Bane, then with the *Los Angeles Herald-Examiner*, and they enthusiastically

agreed. The result was that Burgess and Hoagland approached Dr. Carl Sagan, Director of the Laboratory of Planetary Studies, Cornell University, who was then visiting the Jet Propulsion Laboratory, Pasadena, in connection with Mariner 9. Dr. Sagan had a short while earlier been involved in a conference in the Crimea devoted to the problems of communicating with extraterrestrial intelligences, and together with Dr. Frank Drake, Director of the National Astronomy and Ionosphere Center, Cornell, had designed one type of message that might be used to communicate with an alien intelligence.

Dr. Sagan also was enthusiastic about the idea of a message on Pioneer. He and Dr. Drake designed a plaque, and Linda Salzman Sagan prepared artwork which was presented to the National Aeronautics and Space Administration which accepted it for this first spacecraft from the Solar System into the Galaxy.

The plaque design was etched into a gold-anodized aluminum plate, 15.25 by 22.8 cm

(6 by 9 inches), and 0.127 cm (0.050 inches) thick. This plate was attached to the spacecraft's antenna support struts in a position to help shield it from erosion by interstellar dust (Figure Ep-1).

When Pioneer 10 flew by Jupiter it acquired sufficient kinetic energy to carry it completely out of the Solar System. About 40,000 years hence it will have coasted to the distance of the nearest star, heading in the direction of the constellation of Taurus, the Bull. Somewhere between one and ten billion years from now it may pass through the planetary system of a remote stellar neighbor, one of whose planets may have evolved intelligent life.

If that life possesses sufficient intelligence to detect the Pioneer spacecraft — needing a higher technology than mankind possesses today — it may also have the curiosity and the technical ability to pick up the spacecraft and take it into a laboratory to inspect it. Then the plaque with its message from Earth people should be found and hopefully deciphered.

The plaque tells of Man, where and when the species lived, and its biological form. At top left of the plaque (Figure Ep-2) is a schematic of the hyperfine transition of neutral atomic hydrogen — a universal 'yardstick' — providing a basic unit of both time and physical length throughout the physical universe. As a further size check, the binary equivalent of the decimal number 8 is shown between tote marks indicating the height of the two human figures to be compared with the scale of the spacecraft itself which is also shown in line silhouette on the plaque.

The hydrogen wavelength — about 20.32 cm (8 inches) — multiplied by the binary number representing 8 alongside the woman, gives her height, namely 62.56 cm (64 inches).

The radial pattern to the left of the center of the plaque represents the position of the Sun relative to 14 pulsars and to the center of the Galaxy. The latter direction is indicated by the long horizontal line with no binary digits on it. The binary digits on the other lines denote time. This can be deduced because they represent precision to

184

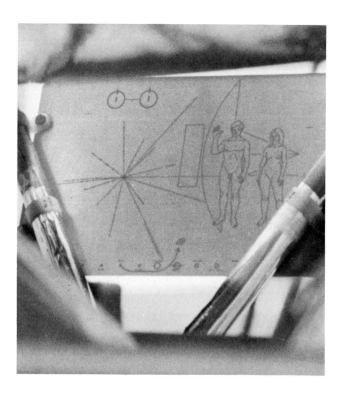

Figure Ep-1. **Photo of the plaque mounted on the spacecraft.**

10 decimal digits, which is unlikely for distances to stellar objects but quite feasible for measurements of time. And from the unit of time established from the hydrogen atom, the extraterrestrial intelligence should be able to deduce that all the times are about one tenth of a second . . . pulsars!

Since the periods of pulsars run down at well established rates they act as galactic clocks. An advanced civilization would be able to search its galactic records and identify the star system from which the spacecraft originated, even if Pioneer is not intercepted for several billions of years.

Below the orientation diagram, as a further aid to identification should the spacecraft be intercepted while our Solar System is still in the galactic records, there is a diagram showing relative distances of the solar planets and identifying the ringed planet Saturn and the planet from which Pioneer originated. After accelerating past the largest planet as shown by a track, the spacecraft is depicted with its antenna pointing back to its origin on the third planet.

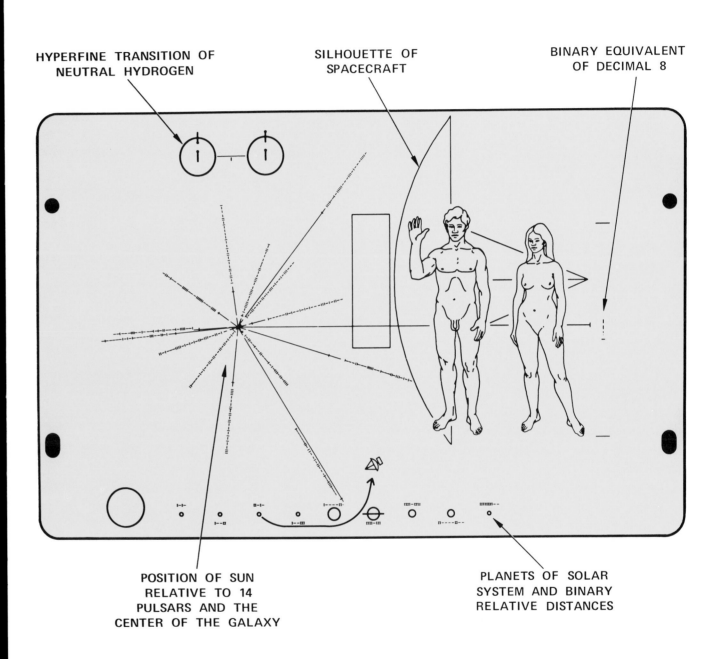

HYPERFINE TRANSITION OF
NEUTRAL HYDROGEN

SILHOUETTE OF
SPACECRAFT

BINARY EQUIVALENT
OF DECIMAL 8

POSITION OF SUN
RELATIVE TO 14
PULSARS AND THE
CENTER OF THE GALAXY

PLANETS OF SOLAR
SYSTEM AND BINARY
RELATIVE DISTANCES

Figure Ep-2. Line drawing of the plaque with explanatory call-outs.

185

Finally the plaque depicts man and woman in what to humans is a characteristic gesture of friendliness but also shows how limbs can be moved and displays the important four fingers and opposing thumb. The figures and physiognomy were carefully chosen and drawn for ethnic neutrality, and no attempt is made to explain to an alien intelligence what may be mysterious differences between two physical types — man and woman.

A similar plaque is carried by Pioneer 11.

As an epilog to the Pioneer mission to Jupiter, the plaque is more than a cold message to an alien life form in the most distant future. It signifies an attribute of mankind that in an era when troubles of war, pollution, clashing idealogies, and serious social and supply problems plague them, men can still think beyond themselves and have the vision to send a message through space and time to intelligence on a star system that perhaps has not yet condensed from a galactic nebula.

The plaque represents at least one intellectual cave painting, a mark of Man, that might survive not only all the caves of Earth, but also the Solar System itself. It is an interstellar stela that shows mankind possesses a spiritual insight beyond the material problems of the age of human emergence.

Appendix 1
The Imaging Photopolarimeter

THE ENTIRE SCIENTIFIC instrument complex of Pioneer was needed to provide the new look at Jupiter. However, it was the imaging mode of the imaging photopolarimeter (IPP) that returned colored images of Jupiter's cloud cover to reveal details never before seen. This appendix provides further technical details of this instrument.

The IPP consists basically of a positionable optics-detector assembly and an electronic equipment housing, supported on a central mounting frame. Special optical materials were selected to retain their transparency even though subjected to Jupiter's radiation belts of trapped energetic protons and electrons.

The optical system (Figure Ap-1) consists of a 2.54-cm (1-inch) diameter Maksutov type telescope, a calcite Wollaston prism polarization analyzer, multilayer filters to separate red and blue components of the reflected light from Jupiter, relay optics, and two dual, continuous channel-multiplier detectors each designed to sense two polarization components in one of two colors (a total of four channels). The field of view can be varied by use of three apertures on a carrier which also carries polarization processing elements (depolarizer and half-wave retardation plate) and an internal calibration lamp.

Analog signals from the detectors are digitized, buffered in the spacecraft's data storage unit, and transmitted together with instrument status information in either of two telemetry formats. After a command into the data taking mode has been received, the electronic logic processor automatically provides all internal commands required to sequence a complete measurement function with

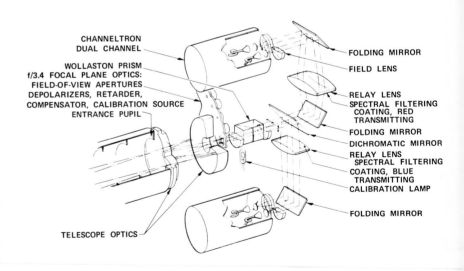

CHANNELTRON
DUAL CHANNEL

WOLLASTON PRISM
f/3.4 FOCAL PLANE OPTICS:
FIELD-OF-VIEW APERTURES
DEPOLARIZERS, RETARDER,
COMPENSATOR, CALIBRATION SOURCE
ENTRANCE PUPIL

FOLDING MIRROR
FIELD LENS

RELAY LENS
SPECTRAL FILTERING
COATING, RED
TRANSMITTING
FOLDING MIRROR
DICHROMATIC MIRROR
RELAY LENS
SPECTRAL FILTERING
COATING, BLUE
TRANSMITTING
CALIBRATION LAMP

FOLDING MIRROR

TELESCOPE OPTICS

Figure Ap-1. The IPP optical system.

187

the IPP and then return the instrument to standby. Additional commands are incorporated to adjust power supply voltages (gain), alter sampling rates, inhibit functions, change the direction in which the telescope steps, and so on.

A field of view of 0.028 degrees square is employed in the imaging mode of the IPP. The field of view is moved slightly (stepped) every roll of the spacecraft, unless inhibited from doing so by command. Step direction can be selected by command. A 6-bit telemetry format provides 64 shades of gray for imaging. In this mode only two of the four detector channels are used, and the light is depolarized prior to detection. Sampling takes place on the dark sky, and the resultant output is used to compensate for zero-level shifts and background caused by the radiation belt environment. Detector output is measured each 0.015 degrees (or 0.03 degrees if so commanded to the low sampling rate) of spacecraft roll, alternating colors. The spacecraft buffer stores imaging data collected over 14 degrees (or 28 degrees in the low sample rate) of each roll.

The manner in which the IPP scans to produce an image is shown in Figure Ap-2. Scan lines, analogous to the horizontal lines in a television system, are produced by the instrument looking in a fixed direction with respect to the spacecraft as the spacecraft spins. The start of each scan is controlled by a series of "spoke" commands which relate the start to the spin position, or, alternatively, the scan can be started automatically by the telescope receiving light from the limb of the planet using the "start data at threshold" mode. The equivalent of television vertical scanning is achieved by either stepping the instrument's telescope 0.5 milliradians with respect to the spin axis between each rotation of the spacecraft or, during the closest approach to Jupiter, holding the telescope fixed and letting the relative motion of spacecraft and Jupiter produce the scanning steps. This means that during the closest approach the scan lines can be overlapping, or have gaps between them, depending upon the relative motions of spacecraft and planet.

In the imaging mode, the data are converted to 64 levels of intensities (6 bits) and stored in a 6144-bit buffer onboard the spacecraft. The instrument overwrites this buffer as it starts each "vertical" scan with each rotation of the spacecraft. The memory read-in time is approximately one-half second, and the spacecraft rotation period is approximately 12.5 seconds, which means that there are approximately 12 seconds available for reading out the data from the memory. To read out these 6144 bits in the 12 seconds that are available requires a data rate of 512 bits per second. The IPP instrument receives 50 percent service rate on the spacecraft's telemetry downlink. Thus a 1024 bits per second telemetry downlink to Earth is the minimum data rate at which all the IPP data taken can be returned to Earth.

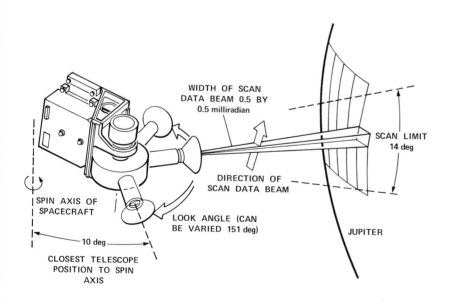

Figure Ap-2. The IPP imaging system.

188

Appendix 2
Technical Details of Jupiter Images

THIS TABLE lists the important parameters regarding the Jovian images taken by Pioneer 10 in the period of four days on either side of closest approach to the planet. The first column gives the sequence of the images, or image number, numbering down to periapsis and up afterward: A images are before periapsis; B images are after periapsis. Missing numbers, e.g., A4 and A24, refer to images of satellites, not listed in this appendix.

The mid time is the time at which the data forming the central line of the image was received on Earth. It is expressed in day of year (DOY), hours, and minutes of Universal Time.

The other columns refer to the position of the spacecraft when the data was taken. Range, measured from the spacecraft to the center of Jupiter, and pixel size, are given in kilometers. The pixel size can be used to assess the resolution limit of a

picture. The phase angle is the angle between the direction from Jupiter to the Sun and the direction from Jupiter to the spacecraft. When the phase angle is zero, a fully illuminated disc is seen. As the angle increases, the terminator moves across the face of the visible disc until at 90° there is a half disc image. Above a phase angle of 90° the illuminated part appears increasingly crescent shaped as the angle approaches its maximum possible value of 180°. The visual effect of changing phase angle is illustrated in Figure 8-1 for Pioneer 10.

The latitude and longitude of the center of the disc as seen by the spacecraft are also given. Negative latitude values refer to the southern hemisphere. Jupiter rotates at slightly different rates depending on the latitude, and there are two commonly used systems for expressing longitude. The longitude in these systems I and II is provided in the last two columns of the table, respectively.

189

Image No. Seq.	Mid time DOY hr min	Range, km	Pixel Size, km	Phase Angle, Degrees	Lat.	Longitude LCM1	LCM2
A104	334 : 2 : 34	4800000	2364	32.8	−6.5	275	233
A103	334 : 3 : 1	4782000	2355	32.8	−6.5	291	249
A102	334 : 3 : 41	4755000	2342	32.8	−6.5	315	273
A101	334 : 6 : 0	4662000	2296	32.6	−6.6	40	357
A100	334 : 6 : 23	4647000	2288	32.6	−6.6	54	11
A99	334 : 7 : 3	4620000	2275	32.6	−6.6	78	35
A98	334 : 7 : 27	4604000	2267	32.5	−6.6	93	50
A97	334 : 8 : 5	4578000	2254	32.5	−6.6	116	73
A96	334 : 8 : 31	4561000	2245	32.5	−6.6	132	88
A95	334 : 9 : 8	4537000	2233	32.4	−6.6	154	110
A94	334 : 9 : 35	4518000	2224	32.4	−6.6	171	127
A93	334 : 10 : 10	4495000	2212	32.4	−6.6	192	148
A92	334 : 10 : 39	4475000	2202	32.3	−6.6	210	165
A91	334 : 11 : 13	4452000	2191	32.3	−6.6	231	186
A90	334 : 11 : 41	4433000	2181	32.3	−6.6	247	203
A89	334 : 12 : 16	4410000	2169	32.2	−6.7	269	224
A88	334 : 17 : 31	4195000	2062	31.9	−6.7	101	54
A87	334 : 18 : 5	4172000	2051	31.8	−6.8	121	74
A86	334 : 18 : 28	4156000	2043	31.8	−6.8	135	88
A85	334 : 19 : 4	4131000	2030	31.7	−6.8	157	110
A84	334 : 19 : 28	4115000	2022	31.7	−6.8	172	124
A83	335 : 2 : 39	3817000	1873	31.1	−6.9	74	24
A82	335 : 3 : 1	3802000	1866	31.1	−6.9	87	37
A81	335 : 3 : 38	3776000	1853	31.0	−6.9	109	59
A80	335 : 4 : 1	3760000	1844	31.0	−7.0	124	74
A79	335 : 4 : 38	3734000	1832	30.9	−7.0	146	96
A78	335 : 5 : 1	3718000	1824	30.9	−7.0	160	109
A77	335 : 5 : 37	3693000	1811	30.8	−7.0	182	131
A76	335 : 6 : 0	3676000	1803	30.8	−7.0	196	145
A75	335 : 9 : 43	3519000	1724	30.4	−7.1	331	280
A74	335 : 10 : 15	3496000	1712	30.3	−7.1	351	299
A73	335 : 10 : 45	3475000	1702	30.3	−7.1	9	317
A72	335 : 11 : 17	3452000	1690	30.2	−7.1	28	336
A71	335 : 11 : 48	3430000	1679	30.2	−7.1	47	355
A70	335 : 12 : 19	3407000	1668	30.1	−7.2	66	14
A69	335 : 12 : 53	3383000	1656	30.0	−7.2	87	34
A68	335 : 14 : 35	3310000	1620	29.8	−7.2	149	95
A67	335 : 15 : 16	3280000	1605	29.7	−7.2	174	120
A66	335 : 15 : 42	3261000	1595	29.7	−7.3	190	136
A65	335 : 16 : 22	3232000	1581	29.6	−7.3	214	160

Image No. Seq.	Mid time DOY hr min	Range, km	Pixel Size, km	Phase Angle, Degrees	Lat.	Longitude LCM1	LCM2
A64	335 : 16 : 50	3212000	1571	29.5	−7.3	231	177
A63	335 : 17 : 29	3184000	1556	29.5	−7.3	255	200
A59	335 : 22 : 2	2984000	1456	28.8	−7.5	60	5
A58	335 : 22 : 27	2965000	1447	28.7	−7.5	76	20
A57	335 : 23 : 5	2937000	1433	28.7	−7.5	99	43
A56	335 : 23 : 34	2916000	1422	28.6	−7.5	116	60
A55	336 : 0 : 14	2886000	1408	28.5	−7.5	140	84
A54	336 : 0 : 41	2866000	1397	28.4	−7.5	157	100
A53	336 : 1 : 21	2836000	1383	28.3	−7.6	181	124
A51	336 : 6 : 55	2584000	1257	27.3	−7.8	23	325
A50	336 : 7 : 31	2557000	1243	27.2	−7.8	45	346
A49	336 : 8 : 11	2525000	1227	27.0	−7.9	69	10
A48	336 : 8 : 48	2497000	1213	26.9	−7.9	92	33
A47	336 : 9 : 30	2465000	1197	26.7	−7.9	117	58
A46	336 : 10 : 7	2436000	1183	26.6	−8.0	139	80
A45	336 : 10 : 48	2404000	1166	26.4	−8.0	165	105
A44	336 : 11 : 25	2375000	1152	26.3	−8.0	187	127
A43	336 : 12 : 6	2343000	1136	26.1	−8.1	211	151
A39	336 : 14 : 33	2227000	1078	25.5	−8.2	301	240
A38	336 : 15 : 10	2198000	1064	25.4	−8.2	323	262
A37	336 : 15 : 55	2161000	1045	25.1	−8.3	350	289
A36	336 : 16 : 33	2131000	1030	25.0	−8.3	13	312
A35	336 : 17 : 21	2092000	1011	24.7	−8.4	42	340
A34	336 : 17 : 59	2061000	995	24.5	−8.4	65	3
A33	336 : 18 : 49	2021000	975	24.3	−8.5	95	33
A32	336 : 19 : 29	1989000	959	24.1	−8.5	119	57
A31	336 : 20 : 18	1948000	939	23.8	−8.6	149	86
A30	336 : 20 : 58	1915000	922	23.6	−8.6	173	110
A29	336 : 21 : 50	1872000	901	23.3	−8.7	204	141
A28	336 : 22 : 31	1837000	883	23.0	−8.8	229	166
A27	337 : 2 : 5	1656000	793	21.5	−9.1	358	293
A26	337 : 2 : 36	1630000	779	21.3	−9.1	16	311
A23	337 : 8 : 32	1313000	621	18.0	−9.9	229	162
A22	337 : 8 : 52	1295000	612	17.8	−9.9	241	174
A21	337 : 9 : 26	1264000	596	17.4	−10.0	261	194
A20	337 : 9 : 42	1248000	589	17.2	−10.0	271	204
A19	337 : 10 : 14	1218000	574	16.9	−10.1	290	223
A18	337 : 10 : 33	1201000	565	16.6	−10.2	301	233
A17	337 : 11 : 5	1170000	550	16.2	−10.3	320	252
A16	337 : 11 : 23	1153000	541	16.0	−10.3	330	263

Image No. Seq.	Mid time DOY hr min	Range, km	Pixel Size, km	Phase Angle, Degrees	Lat.	Longitude LCM1	LCM2
A15	337 : 11 : 56	1122000	526	15.6	−10.4	350	282
A14	337 : 12 : 14	1104000	517	15.4	−10.5	1	293
A13	337 : 12 : 46	1073000	501	15.0	−10.6	20	312
A12	337 : 13 : 5	1055000	492	14.7	−10.7	31	323
A11	337 : 13 : 36	1025000	477	14.3	−10.8	48	340
A10	337 : 13 : 58	1003000	466	14.0	−10.9	61	353
A9	337 : 14 : 47	954000	442	13.4	−11.1	90	22
A8	337 : 15 : 17	924000	427	13.1	−11.2	107	39
A7	337 : 16 : 19	861000	395	12.4	−11.4	143	74
A6	337 : 17 : 5	814000	372	12.1	−11.7	169	100
A5	337 : 18 : 28	726000	328	12.2	−12.1	216	147
A2	338 : 1 : 46	245000	87	66.7	−11.1	58	346
A1	338 : 3 : 8	203000	66	109.5	−2.4	64	352
B1	338 : 8 : 38	504000	217	146.7	13.8	165	91
B6	338 : 16 : 40	1015000	472	124.4	12.5	75	358
B7	338 : 17 : 20	1053000	491	123.5	12.4	98	21
B8	338 : 22 : 26	1341000	635	118.2	11.8	279	200
B9	338 : 23 : 8	1379000	654	117.6	11.7	304	225
B10	338 : 23 : 56	1423000	676	117.0	11.6	333	253
B11	339 : 0 : 50	1472000	700	116.4	11.6	5	286
B12	339 : 1 : 45	1620000	725	115.8	11.5	38	318
B13	339 : 2 : 44	1572000	750	115.2	11.4	73	353
B14	339 : 3 : 23	1606000	767	114.8	11.3	96	16
B15	339 : 3 : 48	1627000	778	114.6	11.3	111	31
B16	339 : 4 : 31	1664000	797	114.2	11.2	137	57
B17	339 : 4 : 54	1684000	807	114.0	11.2	151	70
B18	339 : 5 : 37	1720000	825	113.6	11.2	177	96
B19	339 : 5 : 57	1738000	833	113.4	11.1	189	108
B20	339 : 6 : 40	1774000	852	113.1	11.1	215	134
B21	339 : 7 : 12	1801000	865	112.9	11.0	234	153
B22	339 : 7 : 49	1833000	881	112.6	11.0	256	175
B23	339 : 8 : 9	1849000	889	112.4	11.0	268	186
B24	339 : 9 : 10	1900000	914	112.0	10.9	305	223
B25	339 : 9 : 29	1915000	922	111.9	10.9	316	234
B26	339 : 10 : 15	1953000	941	111.6	10.9	344	262
B27	339 : 10 : 32	1968000	948	111.5	10.8	355	272
B28	339 : 11 : 14	2001000	965	111.2	10.8	19	297
B29	339 : 12 : 3	2041000	985	110.9	10.8	49	326
B30	339 : 12 : 43	2074000	1002	110.7	10.7	74	350
B37	339 : 20 : 30	2444000	1187	108.4	10.4	356	270

Image No. Seq.	Mid time DOY hr min	Range, km	Pixel Size, km	Phase Angle, Degrees	Lat.	Longitude LCM1	Longitude LCM2
B38	339 : 20 : 58	2466000	1197	108.3	10.3	13	287
B39	339 : 21 : 25	2487000	1208	108.2	10.3	29	303
B40	339 : 22 : 26	2533000	1231	108.0	10.3	66	340
B41	339 : 23 : 24	2578000	1253	107.8	10.2	101	14
B42	339 : 23 : 49	2597000	1263	107.7	10.2	116	29
B43	340 : 5 : 28	2853000	1391	106.6	10.0	322	233
B44	340 : 5 : 52	2871000	1400	106.5	10.0	336	248
B45	340 : 7 : 35	2947000	1438	106.2	10.0	39	310
B46	340 : 9 : 12	3019000	1474	105.9	9.9	97	8
B47	340 : 9 : 31	3033000	1481	105.9	9.9	109	19
B48	340 : 9 : 57	3052000	1491	105.8	9.9	125	35
B53	341 : 5 : 37	3893000	1911	103.4	9.5	121	25
B54	341 : 5 : 58	3908000	1918	103.4	9.5	135	38
B55	341 : 6 : 20	3923000	1926	103.4	9.5	148	52
B56	341 : 6 : 56	3948000	1938	103.3	9.5	170	73
B57	341 : 7 : 14	3960000	1945	103.3	9.4	181	84
B58	341 : 7 : 50	3985000	1957	103.2	9.4	203	106
B59	341 : 8 : 9	3998000	1964	103.2	9.4	214	117
B60	341 : 8 : 43	4022000	1975	103.1	9.4	235	138
B61	341 : 9 : 30	4054000	1992	103.1	9.4	263	166
B62	341 : 9 : 55	4071000	2000	103.0	9.4	279	181
B63	341 : 10 : 19	4088000	2009	103.0	9.4	293	196
B66	341 : 16 : 0	4321000	2125	102.6	9.3	141	41
B67	341 : 16 : 20	4335000	2132	102.5	9.3	153	53
B68	341 : 16 : 47	4353000	2141	102.5	9.3	169	69
B69	341 : 17 : 8	4367000	2148	102.5	9.3	182	82
B70	341 : 17 : 36	4386000	2158	102.4	9.3	199	99
B71	341 : 17 : 55	4399000	2164	102.4	9.3	210	110
B72	341 : 18 : 24	4419000	2174	102.4	9.3	228	128
B73	341 : 19 : 25	4459000	2194	102.3	9.3	265	164
B74	341 : 19 : 44	4473000	2201	102.3	9.3	277	176
B75	341 : 20 : 6	4488000	2208	102.3	9.3	290	190
B76	341 : 23 : 45	4635000	2282	102.0	9.2	64	322

The following table lists the important parameters regarding the images of Jupiter taken by Pioneer 11 in the period three days on either side of the closest approach to the planet. C images are before and D images after periapsis. Longitudes are given in System II only (LCM2).

Image No. Seq.	Mid time DOY hr min	Range, km	Pixel Size, km	Phase Angle, Degrees	Lat.	Longitude LCM2
C70	334 : 6 : 48	3891294	1910	45.1	−9.1	138.
C69	334 : 7 : 18	3869879	1900	45.1	−9.1	156.
C68	334 : 7 : 51	3845604	1887	45.1	−9.1	176.
C67	334 : 8 : 12	3830848	1880	45.2	−9.1	188
C66	334 : 8 : 52	3802162	1866	45.2	−9.2	213
C65	334 : 11 : 1	3708544	1819	45.4	−9.3	291
C64	334 : 11 : 52	3672093	1801	45.4	−9.4	321
C63	334 : 12 : 28	3645599	1787	45.5	−9.4	343
C62	334 : 13 : 12	3613628	1771	45.5	−9.5	10
C61	334 : 13 : 37	3595509	1762	65.5	−9.5	25
C60	334 : 14 : 11	3570454	1750	45.6	−9.5	46
C53	334 : 17 : 59	3403095	1666	45.9	−9.8	184
C50	334 : 19 : 38	3329933	1630	46.0	−9.9	243
C49	334 : 20 : 14	3302553	1616	46.0	−10.0	266
C48	334 : 20 : 41	3282693	1606	46.1	−10.0	282
C47	334 : 21 : 37	3240991	1585	46.2	−10.1	316.
C46	334 : 22 : 9	3217310	1573	46.2	−10.1	335
C41	335 : 0 : 55	3092460	1511	46.5	−10.4	75
C40	335 : 2 : 0	3043031	1486	46.6	−10.5	115
C39	335 : 2 : 32	3018510	1474	46.6	−10.5	135
C38	335 : 3 : 10	2989867	1460	46.7	−10.6	157
C37	335 : 4 : 14	2940750	1435	46.8	−10.7	196
C36	335 : 4 : 49	2914046	1422	46.9	−10.8	217
C33	335 : 7 : 52	2773412	1351	47.2	−11.1	328
C32	335 : 8 : 30	2743633	1336	47.3	−11.2	351
C31	335 : 9 : 6	2715618	1322	47.4	−11.2	13
C27	335 : 16 : 30	2363325	1146	48.4	−12.3	282
C26	335 : 17 : 16	2325740	1127	48.5	−12.4	310
C25	335 : 17 : 48	2299710	1114	48.6	−12.5	330
C24	335 : 19 : 2	2239619	1084	48.9	−12.7	14
C23	335 : 19 : 44	2204919	1067	49.0	−12.8	40
C22	335 : 21 : 0	2141985	1036	49.2	−13.0	86
C21	335 : 21 : 43	2106195	1018	49.4	−13.2	112
C20	335 : 22 : 25	2071027	1000	49.5	−13.3	138
C18	336 : 0 : 41	1956270	943	50.0	−13.8	220
C17	336 : 4 : 12	1774242	852	51.0	−14.7	348
C16	336 : 5 : 20	1714067	822	51.3	−15.0	30
C15	336 : 5 : 36	1700113	815	51.4	−15.1	39
C14	336 : 7 : 11	1615214	772	51.9	−15.6	97
C13	336 : 8 : 15	1556648	743	52.3	−16.0	137

194

Image No. Seq.	Mid time DOY hr min	Range, km	Pixel Size, km	Phase Angle, Degrees	Lat.	Longitude LCM2
C11	336 : 10 : 49	1414575	672	53.4	−17.0	231
C9	336 : 13 : 57	1235003	582	55.1	−18.5	345
C8	336 : 15 : 29	1144376	537	56.1	−19.4	42
C7	336 : 17 : 14	1037836	483	57.5	−20.7	106
C6	336 : 18 : 51	935956	433	59.1	−22.1	166
C5	336 : 21 : 26	764812	347	62.6	−25.1	263
C4	336 : 22 : 58	657366	293	65.6	−27.6	321
C3	337 : 0 : 30	545294	237	69.8	−31.0	21
C2	337 : 1 : 54	434832	182	75.7	−39.5	78
C1	337 : 2 : 37	376886	153	80.0	−38.6	108
D1	337 : 9 : 27	375496	152	64.1	51.8	232
D2	337 : 10 : 10	434690	182	59.8	51.2	266
D3	337 : 10 : 39	473362	201	57.6	50.6	288
D4	337 : 12 : 27	610393	270	51.7	48.5	3
D5	337 : 14 : 32	756879	343	47.7	46.5	85
D6	337 : 16 : 34	893309	411	45.0	44.9	164
D8	337 : 19 : 31	1079206	504	42.4	43.1	275
D9	337 : 21 : 55	1222778	576	40.9	42.0	4
D10	337 : 23 : 25	1309664	619	40.1	41.4	59
D11	338 : 3 : 29	1538654	734	38.5	40.0	210
D12	338 : 4 : 21	1585645	757	38.2	39.8	241
D14	338 : 7 : 57	1777382	853	37.3	38.9	13
D15	338 : 9 : 16	1846692	888	37.0	38.7	62
D16	338 : 10 : 20	1901617	915	36.7	38.4	100
D17	338 : 13 : 57	2085307	1007	36.1	37.8	233
D18	338 : 16 : 34	2215675	1072	35.7	37.4	328
D19	338 : 17 : 20	2253495	1091	35.5	37.3	356
D21	338 : 20 : 49	2422939	1176	35.1	36.8	123
D22	338 : 21 : 32	2457420	1193	35.0	36.7	149
D23	338 : 22 : 23	2498412	1214	34.9	36.6	180
D24	338 : 23 : 8	2533882	1232	34.8	36.6	207
D25	339 : 0 : 8	2581602	1255	34.7	36.5	244
D28	339 : 4 : 3	2765661	1347	34.4	36.1	27
D29	339 : 6 : 57	2899829	1414	34.1	35.8	132
D30	339 : 7 : 29	2924294	1427	34.1	35.7	151
D31	339 : 8 : 12	2957037	1443	34.0	35.7	177
D32	339 : 9 : 8	3000238	1465	34.0	35.6	212
D33	339 : 9 : 40	3024145	1477	33.9	35.6	231
D34	339 : 10 : 24	3057503	1493	33.9	35.5	257
D35	339 : 10 : 48	3075892	1503	33.8	35.5	272
D36	339 : 13 : 23	3193034	1561	33.7	35.3	6
D37	339 : 13 : 52	3214703	1572	33.6	35.2	24
D38	339 : 17 : 59	3398493	1664	33.4	35.0	174
D39	339 : 18 : 34	3423783	1676	33.4	34.9	194

Image No. Seq.	Mid time DOY hr min	Range, km	Pixel Size, km	Phase Angle, Degrees	Lat.	Longitude LCM2
D40	339 : 19 : 21	3458503	1694	33.3	34.9	223
D41	339 : 19 : 57	3484746	1707	33.3	34.8	244
D42	339 : 21 : 6	3535636	1732	33.2	34.8	286
D43	339 : 21 : 42	3562414	1746	33.2	34.7	309
D44	339 : 22 : 29	3596173	1763	33.2	34.7	337
D45	339 : 23 : 8	3625028	1777	33.1	34.7	1
D49	340 : 2 : 41	3779177	1854	33.0	34.5	129
D50	340 : 3 : 35	3818033	1874	32.9	34.4	162
D51	340 : 4 : 14	3846085	1888	32.9	34.4	186

Appendix 3
The Pioneer Jupiter Team

PIONEER PROJECT MANAGEMENT

Office of Space Science

John E. Naugle . . . . Associate Administrator for OSS
Vincent L. Johnson . . . . .Deputy Associate Administrator for OSS
Robert S. Kraemer . . . . Director, Planetary Programs
S. Ichtiaque Rasool . . . . Deputy Director, Planetary Programs
Fred D. Kochendorfer . . . . .Pioneer Program Manager
Thomas P. Dallow . . . . Pioneer Program Engineer
Albert G. Opp .Pioneer Program Scientist
Joseph B. Mahon . . . . Director, Launch Vehicle Programs
T. Bland Norris . . . . Manager, Medium Launch Vehicles
F. Robert Schmidt . . . . Manager, Atlas-Centaur

Office of Tracking and Data Acquisition

Gerald M. Truszynski . . . . Associate Administrator for OTDA
Arnold C. Belcher . . . . .Network Operations
Maurice E. Binkley . . . . .Network Support

Ames Research Center, Mountain View, California

Hans Mark . . . . Center Director
C. A. Syvertson . . . . Deputy Director
John V. Foster . . . . Director of Development
Charles F. Hall . . . . Pioneer Project Manager
John H. Wolfe . . . . Pioneer Project Scientist
Ralph W. Holtzclaw . . . . .Pioneer Spacecraft System Manager
Joseph E. Lepetich . . . . Pioneer Experiment System Manager
Robert R. Nunamaker . . . . Pioneer Mission Operations System Manager

Ames Research Center (Continued)

J. Richard Spahr . . . . Management Control
Robert U. Hofstetter . . . . Mission Analysis and Launch Coordination
Norman J. Martin . . . . Mission Control Manager
Richard O. Fimmel . . . . Science Chief
Gilbert A. Schroeder . . . . Spacecraft Chief
Thomas L. Bridges . . . . Data Handling Manager
Arthur C. Wilbur . . . . Nuclear Power
Eldon W. Kaser . . . . Contracts
John R. Mulkern, Henry Asch, Standish R. Benbow
Roger O. Convertino, and George E. DeYoung . . . . Reliability and Quality Assurance
Ernest J. Iufer . . . . Magnetics

Jet Propulsion Laboratory, Pasadena, California

William H. Pickering . . . . .Director, Jet Propulsion Laboratory
Nicholas A. Renzetti . . . . Tracking and Data System Manager
Richard B. Miller . . . . Deep Space Network Manager for Pioneer
Robert E. Ryan . . . . Pioneer Mission Operations Support Coordinator

Lewis Research Center, Cleveland, Ohio

Bruce T. Lundin . . . . Center Director
Edmund R. Jonash . . . . Chief, Launch Vehicles Division
Daniel J. Shramo . . . . Atlas-Centaur Project Manager
Edwin T. Muckley . . . . Centaur Project Engineer

Kennedy Space Center, Florida

Kurt H. Debus . . . . Center Director
John J. Neilon . . . . Director, Unmanned Launch Operations
John D. Gossett . . . . Chief, Centaur Operations Branch
Donald C. Sheppard . . . . Chief, Spacecraft Operations Branch
Hugh A. Weston . . . . Delta Project Manager (For Third Stage)
James W. Johnson . . . . Manager, Pioneer Operations
William R. Fletcher, Jr. . . . . Spacecraft Coordinator

AEC Space Nuclear Systems Division

David S. Gabriel . . . . Division Director
Glenn A. Newby . . . . Assistant Director for Space Electric Power
Harold Jaffe . . . . Chief, Isotope Power Systems Projects Branch
William C. Remini and Bernard Rock . . . . SNAP 19/Pioneer RTG Program Managers

TRW Systems Group

Bernard J. O'Brien . . . . Pioneer Project Manager

PIONEER PROJECT STAFF

Bridges, Thomas L.

Canning, Thomas N.
Chin, Benny
Christiansen, Robert A.
Cowley, John R., Jr.

Dickerson, Lewis W.
Dyer, John W.

Edens, Robert L.

Fimmel, Richard O.
Frank, Joseph L.
Funkhouser, Hallie M.

Garden, William O., Jr.
Gittelson, Robert S.
Givens, John J.
Gowdry, Maurice V.

Hall, Charles F.
Hightower, William D.
Hofstetter, Robert U.
Hogan, Robert P.
Holtzclaw, Ralph W.

James, George C.
Jesse, Eugene
Johnson, Richard D.

Keller, Carl H.

Lepetich, Joseph E.
Levin, Paul E.
Lozier, David W.

Maghan, Jean E.
Mandell, Arthur
Manning, Barbara J.
Martin, Norman J.
McKellar, Donald B.

Natwick, Arvid S.
Nothwang, George J.
Nunamaker, Robert R.

Park, Edwin G., Jr.
Peckham, Lucy M.
Phillips, James R.
Polaski, Louis J.
Porter, Dennis L.
Prevost, Florence Y.

Ramos, Ruben
Rosen, Eugene
Rubenzer, Jon A.

Schimmel, George S.
Schroeder, Gilbert A.
Shillinger, George L.
Sinnott, David B.
Somer, Eva S.
Sommer, Simon C.
Spahr, J. Richard
Sperans, Joel

Thorley, Gary W.
Tischler, Edward
Twarowski, Richard J.

Weber, Theodore T.
Wilbur, Jane G.
Wilhelmi, Alvin J.
Wirth, Manfred N.
Wong, Thomas

Yee, Layton
Zimmerman, Ellen L.

EXPERIMENTS AND INVESTIGATORS

Magnetic Fields Experiment

Principal Investigator . . . . Edward J. Smith
Jet Propulsion Laboratory, Pasadena, California

Coinvestigators . . . . Palmer Dyal
David S. Colburn
NASA-Ames Research Center, Mountain View, California

Charles P. Sonett
University of Arizona

Douglas E. Jones
Brigham Young University, Provo, Utah

Paul J. Coleman, Jr.
University of California at Los Angeles

Leverett Davis, Jr.
California Institute of Technology, Pasadena

Plasma Analyzer Experiment

Principal Investigator . . . . John H. Wolfe
NASA-Ames Research Center

Coinvestigators . . . . .Louis A. Frank
University of Iowa, Iowa City

John Mihalov
H. Collard
D. D. McKibbin
NASA-Ames Research Center

Reimar Lüst
Max-Planck-Institute fur Physik
und Astrophysik
Garching, Germany

Devrie Intriligator
University of Southern California

William C. Feldman
Los Alamos Scientific Laboratory, New Mexico

Charged Particle Composition Experiment

Principal Investigator . . . . John A. Simpson
University of Chicago

Coinvestigators . . . . Joseph J. O'Gallagher
University of Maryland, College Park

Anthony J. Tuzzolino
University of Chicago

Cosmic Ray Energy Spectra Experiment

Principal Investigator . . . . Frank B. McDonald
NASA-Goddard Space Flight Center, Greenbelt, Maryland

Coinvestigators . . . . Kenneth G. McCracken
Minerals Research Laboratory, North Ryde, Australia

William R. Webber
Edmond C. Roelof
University of New Hampshire, Durham

Bonnard J. Teegarden
James H. Trainor
NASA-Goddard Space Flight Center

Jovian Charged Particles Experiment

Principal Investigator . . . . James A. Van Allen
University of Iowa, Iowa City

Jovian Trapped Radiation Experiment

Principal Investigator . . . . R. Walker Fillius
University of California at San Diego

Coinvestigator . . . . Carl E. McIlwain
University of California at San Diego

Asteroid-Meteoroid Astronomy Experiment

Principal Investigator . . . . Robert K. Soberman
General Electric Company, Philadelphia
Drexel University, Philadelphia

Coinvestigator . . . . Herbert A. Zook
NASA-Manned Spacecraft Center, Houston, Texas

Meteoroid Detection Experiment

Principal Investigator . . . . William H. Kinard
NASA-Langley Research Center, Hampton, Virginia

Coinvestigators . . . . Robert L. O'Neal
José M. Alvarez
Donald H. Humes
Richard E. Turner
NASA-Langley Research Center

Celestial Mechanics Experiment

Principal Investigator . . . . John D. Anderson
Jet Propulsion Laboratory

Coinvestigator .George W. Null
Jet Propulsion Laboratory

Ultraviolet Photometry Experiment

Principal Investigator . . . . Darrell L. Judge
University of Southern California, Los Angeles

Coinvestigator . . . . Robert W. Carlson
University of Southern California

Imaging Photopolarimetry Experiment

Principal Investigator . . . . .Tom Gehrels
University of Arizona, Tucson

Co-Investigators . . . . Martin Tomasko
Charles Blenman, Jr.
Charles E. KenKnight
William Swindell
University of Arizona

David L. Coffeen
Goddard Institute for Space Studies, New York City

Robert F. Hummer
Santa Barbara Research Center

Jerry Weinberg
State University of New York, Albany

Martha Hanner
Max Planck Institut, Heidelberg, Germany

Jovian Infrared Thermal Structure Experiment

Principal Investigator . . . . Guido Münch
California Institute of Technology

Coinvestigators . . . . Gerry Neugebauer
California Institute of Technology

Stillman C. Chase
Santa Barbara Research Center

Laurence M. Trafton
University of Texas, Austin, Texas

S-Band Occultation Experiment

Principal Investigator . . . . .Arvydas J. Kliore
Jet Propulsion Laboratory

Coinvestigators . . . . Gunnar Fjeldbo
Dan L. Cain
Boris L. Seidel
Jet Propulsion Laboratory

S. Ichtiaque Rasool
NASA-Headquarters, Washington, D.C.

PIONEER CONTRACTORS

Bendix Field Engineering Corporation, Columbia, Maryland

Walter L. Natzic . . . . Manager, Advanced Data Systems
Thomas F. Groves . . . . .Program Manager
Michael R. Brunofski . . . . Operations Manager
Beverly E. Spencer . . . . .Data Processing Manager
Dennis D. Faherty . . . . .Software Systems Manager

Agpawa, Joseph J.
Andrews, Charles
Araiza, Ruben L.

Barton, Herbert D.
Baumgartner Bernetha B.
Benjamin, Darryl K.
Blanchard, Dennis C.
Boyd, Charles F.
Brownlee, Jamie G.
Brunofski, Michael R.
Buttenhoff, Michael F.

Campbell, Shelby H.
Cox, Henry G.

Dangaran, Richard D.
Davidson, Judith K.
Dreibus, Michael J.

Erickson, Joe M.
Eskridge, James

Faherty, Dennis D.
Fullerton, Jack A.

Gilbert, Carey S.
Goff, Steven L.
Golas, Joseph A.
Groves, Thomas F.

Hernandez, Raymond A.

Irving, Thomas J.

Jacobson, Gerald N.
Jednorozec, Krev C.
Johnson, Lonnie A.

Kapp, Richard V.
Kusalo, Sally A.

Levy, David J.

McCoy, Frank A.
McGhan, James N.
Mearns, John G.
Mitchell, Tanner W.
Moore, Fredrick L.

Natzic, Walter L.

Opachko Elaine A.

Parrish, Janice D.
Peek, Terry S.
Petersen, Lilly R.
Porche, William D.

Ragle, John O.
Reese, Matthias
Revillar, Joanne
Rork, Jon E.
Rose, David B.

Sandoval, Randolph A.
Schmidt, Marylee M.
Seagraves, David A.
Seay, Rose G.
Smith, Sandra L.
Spalding, Thomas A.
Spencer, Beverly E.
Stagi, Angie
Stoloff, Michael J.

Thissell, James D.
Tydell, Ilse K.

van der Veen, Larry C.

Weaver, Ronald L.
West, Claude M.
Whelan, Patrick J.
White, Sandra C.
Woody, Raymond L.

Yamamoto, Stanley M.
Yeager, William J.

PIONEER CONTRACTORS

Contractor	Item
Allen Design Burbank, Calif.	Propellant Valves
Amelco Semiconductor Mountain View, Calif.	Integrated Circuits
Analog Technology Corporation Pasadena, Calif.	Ultraviolet Photometry
Bendix Corporation Columbia, Md.	Mission Operations and Software
Bendix Mosaic Fabrication Division Sturbridge, Mass.	Fiber Optics
Computer Communications Inc. Inglewood, Calif.	Communication Stations
Data Products Corp. Woodland Hills, Calif.	ADP Line Printer
Edcliff Instrument Division Systron Donner Monrovia, Calif.	Despin Sensor Assembly
Electra Midland Corp. Cermatrik Division San Diego, Calif.	Current Limiters
Electronic Memories Division of Electronic Memories and Magnetics Corp. Hawthorne, Calif.	Memory Storage Units
EMR Telemetry Division Weston Instruments Inc. Sarasota, Fla.	Telemetry Decommutation Display Equipment
Frequency Electronics Inc. New Hyde Park, N.Y.	Oscillator (TCXO)
General Dynamics Convair Division San Diego, Calif.	Launch Vehicle — First and Second Stages
General Electric Company Philadelphia, Pa.	Asteroid/Meteoroid Detector

Holex Inc. Hollister, Calif.	Explosive Cartridge
Honeywell, Inc. Radiation Center Lexington, Mass.	Sun Sensor Assemblies
Jet Propulsion Laboratory Pasadena, Calif.	Helium Vector Magnetometer
Los Alamos Scientific Laboratory Los Alamos, N.M.	RTG Fuel Discs
McDonnell-Douglas Corp. Astronautics Company Huntington Beach, Calif.	Launch Vehicle – Third Stage Motor
Mound Laboratories Miamisburg, Ohio	Radioisotope Heater Unit Capsules, RTG Fuel and Capsules
Pratt and Whitney Aircraft Co. East Hartford, Conn.	Launch Vehicle – Second Stage Motor
Pressure Systems Inc. Los Angeles, Calif.	Propellant Tanks
Rockwell International Rocketdyne Division Canoga Park, Calif.	Launch Vehicle – First Stage Motor
Santa Barbara Research Center Santa Barbara, Calif.	Imaging Photopolarimeter and Infrared Radiometer
Siliconix Inc. Santa Clara, Calif.	Integrated Circuits
Teledyne Isotopes Germantown, Md.	Radioisotope Thermoelectric Generators (RTGs)
Teledyne Microwave Sunnyvale, Calif.	RF Transfer Switch
Texas Instruments Dallas, Texas	Integrated Circuits
Thiokol Chemical Company Elkton, Md.	Launch Vehicle – Third Stage Motor
Time Zero Corporation Torrance, Calif.	Plasma Analyzer and Magnetometer Electronics

TRW Systems Group TRW Inc. Redondo Beach, Calif.	Spacecraft
United Detector Technology Inc. Santa Monica, Calif.	Silicon Photo Detectors
University of California at San Diego San Diego, Calif.	Trapped Radiation Detector
University of Chicago Chicago, Ill.	Charged Particle Instrument
University of Iowa Iowa City, Ia.	Geiger Tube Telescope
Watkins-Johnson Co. Palo Alto, Calif.	Traveling Wave Tube Amplifier
Wavecom Inc. Chatsworth, Calif.	Diplexer Assemblies
Xerox Data Systems El Segundo, Calif.	Computer Systems
Yardney Electric Corp. Pawcatuck, Conn.	Silver-Cadmium Battery Cells

Appendix 4
The 1974 Pioneer 10 Award Recipients

"The achievements of Pioneer 10 would not have been possible without the dedicated hard work of many, many people. All of them — in NASA, in industry, and in the scientific community — have our appreciation and admiration for their parts in making Pioneer 10 the success it has been. As Administrator of NASA, I take great pride in giving those receiving awards today and the entire Pioneer 10 team my congratulations for a job well done."

James C. Fletcher
August 16, 1974

DISTINGUISHED SERVICE MEDAL

Charles F. Hall

EXCEPTIONAL SERVICE MEDALS

Richard O. Fimmel
John V. Foster
Robert U. Hofstetter
Ralph W. Holtzclaw
Harold Jaffe
James W. Johnson
Eldon W. Kaser
William E. Kirhofer
Fred D. Kochendorfer
Joseph E. Lepetich
Norman J. Martin
Edwin T. Muckley
Robert R. Nunamaker
Alfred J. Siegmeth
Arthur C. Wilbur

EXCEPTIONAL SCIENTIFIC ACHIEVEMENT MEDALS

John D. Anderson
R. Walker Fillius
Tom Gehrels
Darrell L. Judge
William H. Kinard
Guido Münch
James H. Trainor
James A. Van Allen

PUBLIC SERVICE AWARD

William J. Dixon
Herbert A. Lassen
Walter L. Natzic
Bernard J. O'Brien
William F. Sheehan
Louis A. Watts

PUBLIC SERVICE GROUP ACHIEVEMENT AWARDS

Pioneer 10 Team TRW Systems Group
Pioneer 10 Radioisotope Thermoelectric Generator Contractor Team
Pioneer 10 Team, Bendix Field Engineering Corporation
Pioneer 10 Scientific Instrument Team

GROUP ACHIEVEMENT AWARDS

Ames Pioneer 10 Scientific Instruments Team
Ames Pioneer 10 Spacecraft Team
Ames Pioneer 10 Mission Analysis and Launch Operations Team
Ames Pioneer 10 Mission Operations Team
Ames Pioneer 10 Project Management Team
Ames Pioneer 10 Contracts Team
Ames Research Center Support Groups
Pioneer 10 Mission Analysis Team, Jet Propulsion Laboratory
Pioneer 10 Ground Data System Team, Jet Propulsion Laboratory
Pioneer 10 RTG Team, Atomic Energy Commission
Pioneer 10 Radio Science Team
Pioneer 10 Headquarters Staff Support Group

Arvydas J. Kliore, Edward J. Smith, and John H. Wolfe were also nominated for the Exceptional Scientific Achievement Award. However, since NASA makes only one such award to an individual, these principal investigators did not receive the award again for their work on Pioneer 10. John A. Simpson was nominated for his work in connection with both Pioneer 10 and Mariner 10 and elected to accept the award for Mariner.

SUGGESTIONS FOR FURTHER READING

Acuna, M. H.; and Ness, N. F.: The Complex Magnetic Field of Jupiter, Goddard Space Flight Center Publication X-690-75-42, February 1975.

Anon.: Encounter with Jupiter, *Astronomy*, v. 2, no. 2, Feb. 1974, pp. 4–18.

Anon.: The Great Red Spot, *Astronomy*, v. 3, Aug. 1975, pp. 22–23.

Baker, D.: Report from Jupiter – 2, *Spaceflight*, v. 17, March 1975, pp. 102–107.

Beckman, J. C.; Hyde, J. R.; and Rasool, S. I.: Exploring Jupiter and its Satellites with an Orbiter, *Astronautics and Aeronautics*, v. 12, no. 9, Sept. 1974, pp. 24–35.

Brice, N.; and McDonough, T. R.: Jupiter's Radiation Belts, *Icarus*, v. 18, no. 2, Feb. 1973, pp. 206–219.

Brown, R. A.; Yung, Y. L.: Io, its atmosphere and optical emissions, Jupiter, The Giant Planet, University of Arizona Press, 1976.

Burgess E.: A Second Look at Jupiter, *New Scientist*, v. 64, 12 Dec. 1974, pp. 804–806.

Burgess, E.: *Space Probe*, the Pioneer Jupiter Spacecraft, McGraw-Hill Encyclopedia of Science and Technology Yearbook, 1975.

Burgess, E.: The New Frontier, Pioneer to Jupiter, Series of NASA Education Pamphlets for Schools, 1973/4.

Cameron, A. G. W.: The Outer Solar System, *Science*, v. 180, no. 4087, 18 May 1973, pp. 701–708.

Coffeen, D. L.: Pioneer 10 Observations of Jupiter: An Appeal for Ground-Based Coverage, *Icarus*, v. 20, 1973, pp. 52–53.

Cruikshank, D. P.; Morrison, D.: The Galilean Satellites of Jupiter, *Scientific American*, May 1976, pp. 108–116.

Dickinson, T.: Missions to the Giant Planets, *Astronomy*, v. 3, February 1975, pp. 20–32.

Divine, N., et al.: *The Planet Jupiter* (1970), Space Vehicle Design Criteria (Environment), NASA (Washington, D.C.), Rept. no. SP-8069, Dec. 1971, NASA N72-17909, (NTIS $3.00), 90 pp.

Dyer, J. W.: Pioneer 11's Encounter with Jupiter and Mission to Saturn, International Astronautical Federation paper 75-178, Lisbon, Sept. 1975.

Fillius, W.; McIlwain, C.; Mogro-Campero, A.; and Steinberg, G: Pitch Angle Scattering as an Important Loss Mechanism for Energetic Electrons in the Inner Radiation Belt of Jupiter; *Geophysical Research Letters*, in press 1975.

Fountain, J. W., et al.: Jupiter's Clouds, *Science*, v. 184, 21 June 1974, pp. 1279–1281.

Franklin, K. L.: Radio Waves From Jupiter, *Scientific American*, v. 211, no. 1, July 1964, pp. 35–42.

Gehrels, T.; Suomi, V. E.; and Kraus, R. J.: The Capabilities of the Spin-Scan Imaging Technique, *Space Research*, v. XII, 1972, p. 1765.

Gehrels, T.: The Flyby of Jupiter, *Sky and Telescope*, Feb. 1974.

Gehrels, T. (Editor): Jupiter, the Giant Planet, University of Arizona Press, 1976.

Gierasch, P. J.: Jupiter's Cloud Bands, *Icarus*, v. 19, no. 4, Aug. 1973, pp. 482–494.

Hanner, M. S.; and Weinberg, J. L.: Gegenschein Observations from Pioneer 10, *Sky and Telescope*, v. 45, April 1973.

Hanner, M. S.; and Weinberg, J. L.: Changes in Zodiacal Light With Heliocentric Distance: Preliminary Results From Pioneer 10, COSPAR Paper C.38, May 1973, Konstanz.

Hartmann, W. K.: Saturn – The New Frontier, *Astronomy*, v. 3, January 1975, pp. 26–31.

Hide, R.: Jupiter's Great Red Spot, *Scientific American*, v. 218, no. 2, Feb. 1968, pp. 74–82.

Hide, R.: Jupiter and Saturn, The Planets Today, Proc. Royal Society, London, v. A336, 1974, pp. 63–84.

Hubbard, W. B.; Jokipii, J. R.: New Studies of Jupiter, *Sky and Telescope*, v. 50, October 1975, pp. 212–216.

Hunt, G.; Burgess, E.: Jupiter, Some Conclusions and Questions, *New Scientist*, v. 68, 6 Nov. 1975, pp. 326–327.

Ingersoll, A. P.: Jupiter's Great Red Spot: A Free Atmospheric Vortex, *Science*, v. 182, pp. 1346–1348, 28 December 1973.

Ingersoll, A. P.: The Atmosphere of Jupiter, *Space Science Reviews*, vol. 23, 1975, pp. 206–242.

Ingersoll, A. P.: The Meteorology of Jupiter, *Scientific American*, March 1976, pp. 46–56.

Jastrow, R.; and Rasool, S. I.: The Planet Jupiter, *Science Journal*, v. 3, no. 9, Sept. 1967, pp. 50–54.

Judge, D. L.; Carlson, R. W.; Susuki, K.; and Morse, A. L.: Initial Pioneer 10 Results on the Interplanetary and Interstellar Hydrogen and Helium Glow, *Proceedings of the American Physical Society*, Winter 1972.

Keay, C. S. L., *et al.*: Infrared Maps of Jupiter, *Sky and Telescope*, v. 44, no. 5, Nov. 1972, pp. 296–297.

KenKnight, C. E.: Observations in the Asteroid Belt With the Imaging Photopolarimeter of Pioneer F and G, Physical Studies of the Minor Planets, NASA SP-267, 1971, pp. 633–637.

Kliore, A. J.; Woiceshyn, P. M.: Structure of the Atmosphere of Jupiter From Pioneer 10 and 11 Radio Occultations Measurements, Jupiter, the Giant Planet, University of Arizona Press, 1976.

Kuiper, G. P.: Lunar and Planetary Laboratory Studies of Jupiter, *Sky and Telescope*, v. 43, Jan. 1972, pp. 4–8; v. 43, Feb. 1972, pp. 75–81.

Lewis, J. S.: The Outer Planets, Ch. VI, Man and the Cosmos, W. W. Norton and Company, N.Y., 1975.

Martin, A. R.: Missions to Jupiter-1, *Spaceflight*, v. 14, no. 8, Aug. 1972, pp. 294–299.

Martin, A. R.: Missions to Jupiter-2, *Spaceflight*, v. 14, no. 9, Sept. 1972, pp. 325–332.

McDonald, D.: Encounter with a Giant, A Program for Planetariums, NASA, Ames Research Center, Jan. 1974.

Michaux, C. M., *et al.*: *Handbook of the Physical Properties of the Planet Jupiter*, Douglas Aircraft Co. (Santa Monica, Calif.), Rept. no. NASA SP-3031, 1967, NASA N67-26559, (GPO $0.60), 142 pp.

Miller, R. B.: Pioneer 10 and 11 Mission Support, NASA Technical Report 32-1526, v. XVI, The Deep Space Network, Aug. 15, 1973, pp. 15–21.

Mogro-Campero, Antonio; Fillius, R. W.; and McIlwain, C. E.: Electrons and Protons in Jupiter's Radiation Belts, COSPAR Proceedings, 1974, Sao Paulo.

Molton, P. M.: Exobiology, Jupiter and Life, *Spaceflight*, v. 14, no. 6, June 1972, pp. 220–223.

Morrison, D., Burns, J. A.: The Jovian Satellites, Jupiter, The Giant Planet, University of Arizona Press, 1976.

Ness, N. F.; Behannon, K. W.; Lepping, R. P., Whang, Y. C.: Magnetic Field of Mercury Confirmed, *Nature*, May 1975.

Neste, S. L., Ph.D. Thesis: An Experimental Model of the Asteroid/Meteoroid Environment From 1.0 to 3.5 AU – Its Characteristics and Implications, Drexel University Library, Aug. 1974.

Newburn, R. L., Jr.; and Gulkis, S.: A Survey of the Outer Planets Jupiter, Saturn, Uranus, Neptune, Pluto, and Their Satellites, *Space Science Reviews*, v. 14, no. 2, Feb. 1973, pp. 179–271.

Owen, T.: The Atmosphere of Jupiter, *Science*, v. 167, no. 3926, 27 March 1970, pp. 1675–1681.

Pellicori, S. F., *et al.*: Pioneer Imaging Photopolarimeter Optical System, *Applied Optics*, v. 12, no. 6, June 1973, pp. 1246–1258.

The Pioneer Mission to Jupiter, NASA (Washington, D.C.), Rept. no. SP-268, 1971, NASA N71-32366, (GPO $0.30), 48 pp.

Prasad, S. S.; and Capone, L. A.: The Jovian Ionosphere: Composition and Temperatures, *Icarus*, v. 15, no. 1, Aug. 1971, pp. 45–55.

Reese, E. J.: Jupiter: Its Red Spot and Disturbances in 1970-71, *Icarus*, v. 17, no. 1, Aug. 1972, pp. 57–72.

Sagan, C.: Titan, *Astronomy*, v. 3, March 1975, pp. 4–9.

Sagan, C., *et al.*: A Message From Earth (Plaque on Pioneer 10), *Science*, v. 175, no. 4024, 25 Feb. 1972, pp. 881–884.

Sentman, D. D., Van Allen, J. A.: Recirculation of Energetic Particles in Jupiter's Magnetosphere, *Geophysical Research Letters*, in press 1975.

Shimizu, M.: The Upper Atmosphere of Jupiter, *Icarus*, v. 14, no. 2, April 1971, pp. 273–281.

Simmons, H. T.: Mighty Jupiter Could Be a Star That Didn't Make It, *Smithsonian*, v. 5, no. 6, Sept. 1974, pp. 30–39.

Simpson, J. A., McKibben, R. B.: Dynamics of the Jovian Magnetosphere and Energetic Particle Radiation, Jupiter, The Giant Planet, University of Arizona Press, 1976.

Smith, E. J., Connor, B. V., Foster, G. T. Jr.: Measuring the Magnetic Fields of Jupiter and the Outer Solar System, *IEEE Transactions on Magnetics*, v. MAG-11, July 1975, pp. 962–980.

Smith, E. J., Davis, L. Jr., Jones, D. E.: Jupiter's Magnetic Field and Magnetosphere, Jupiter, the Giant Planet, University of Arizona Press, 1976.

Smith, E. J., *et al.*: Jovian Electron Bursts: Correlation with the Interplanetary Field Direction and Hydrodynamic Waves, *Journal of Geophysical Research*, in press 1976.

Soberman, R. K.; Neste, S. L.; and Petty, A. F.: Asteroid Detection From Pioneer F/G, Physical Studies of the Minor Planets, NASA SP-267, 1971, pp. 617–631.

Streett, W. B., *et al.*: On the Structure and Motions of Jupiter's Red Spot, *Icarus*, v. 14, no. 3, June 1971, pp. 319-342.

Strobel, D. F.: The Photochemistry of Hydrocarbons in the Jovian Atmosphere, *Journal of the Atmospheric Sciences*, v. 30, no. 3, April 1973, pp. 489–498.

Thomsen, M. F.; and Van Allen, J. A.: Galactic Cosmic Ray Intensity 0.99 to 5.26 A.U. from the Sun, University of Iowa paper 75-30, August 1975.

Van Allen, J. A.: Interplanetary Particles and Fields, *Scientific American*, v. 233, September 1975.

Van Allen, J. A.: High-Energy Particles in the Jovian Magnetosphere, Jupiter, the Giant Planet, University of Arizona Press, 1976.

Van Allen, J. A., *et al.*: Pioneer 11 Observations of Energetic Particles in the Jovian Magnetosphere, *Science*, v. 188, 2 May 1975, pp. 459–462.

Van Allen, J. A.; and Randall, R. F.: Jupiter's Magnetosphere as Observed with Pioneer 10, *Astronautics and Aeronautics*, July/August 1974, pp. 14–21.

Various authors: *Journal of Geophysical Research*, Special Pioneer 10 issue containing reports on all the experiments, v. 79, Sept. 1, 1974, pp. 3489–3694.

Various authors: *Science*, Reports of all the science experiments on Pioneer 10 and of the ground based experiments, v. 183, January 25, 1974, pp. 301–324.

Various authors: *Science*, Reports of all the science experiments on Pioneer 11 and of the ground based experiments, v. 188, 2 May 1975, pp. 445–477.

Weinberg, J. L.; Hanner, M. S.; Mann, H. M.; Hutchinson, P. B.; and Fimmel, R. O.: Observations of Zodiacal Light From the Pioneer 10 Asteroid – Jupiter Probe: Preliminary Results, *Space Research XIII*, Akademie-Verlag, Berlin, 1973.

Westphal, J. A.; Matthews, K.; and Terrile, R. J.: Five-Micron Pictures of Jupiter, *Astrophysical Journal*, v. 188, no. 3, p. L111, March 15, 1974.

Williams, G. P.: Jupiter's Atmospheric Circulation, *Nature*, v. 257, 30 Oct. 1975, p. 778.

Woolfe, J.: Jupiter, *Scientific American*, v. 233, Sept. 1975, pp. 118–126.

Index

214